Happy Christm

Dad,

Love from -

THE DRIFTWOOD FIDDLE
and other stories

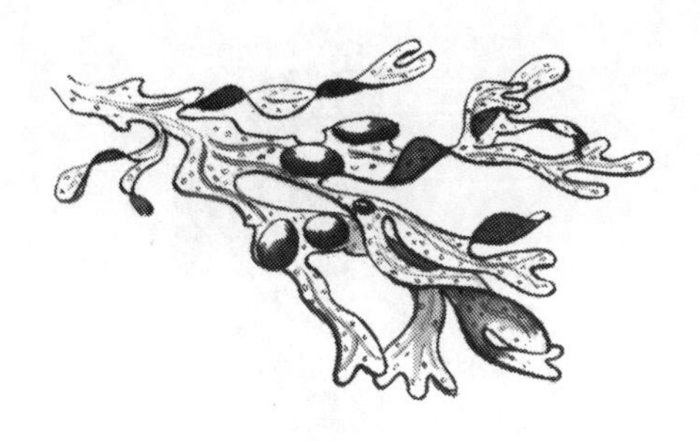

THE DRIFTWOOD FIDDLE
and other stories
Harry Berry

Compiled by Paul Heppleston

Illustrated by Isobel Gardner

ORKNEY PRESS
KIRKWALL 1990

Published by The Orkney Press Ltd 1990.
12 Craigiefield Park, St Ola, Kirkwall, Orkney.

Typeset by Dog & Bone, Glasgow.
Designed by Alasdair Gray.

Printed by The Orcadian, Victoria Street,
Kirkwall, Orkney.

Front cover illustration by Isobel Gardner. The paintings reproduced on the back cover are all by Harry Berry, from the collection of the late Dr Sydney Peace of Kirkwall, and are reproduced here by kind permission of Mrs Helen Peace. Photography of paintings by Richard Welsby.
Cover design by Iain Ashman

ISBN 0 907618 23 5

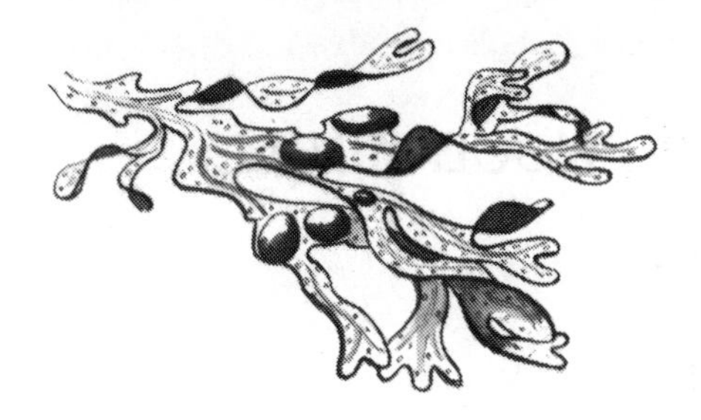

TABLE OF

CONTENTS

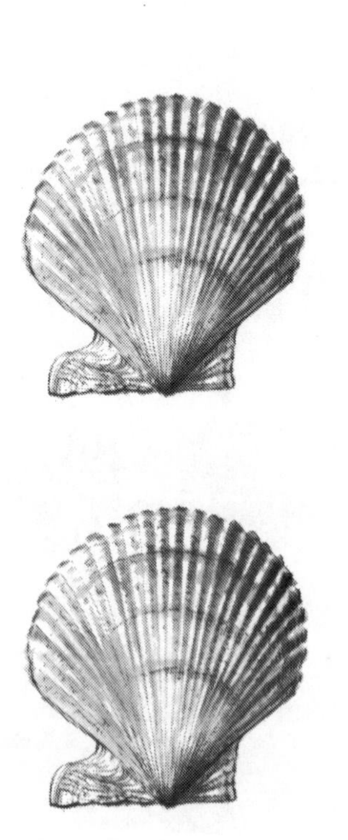

FOREWORD
by Jimmie Macgregor

FOR MOST PEOPLE, the Old Man of Hoy is that incredible towering chimney of Orcadian rock, now familiar to us through television, and stomach-churning pictures of mini-aturised climbers slowly crawling up its dizzying chimneys, fissures and faces. For me, the Old Man of Hoy is Harry Berry. I encountered him many years ago, while on my first concert tour of the Orkney Isles. Meeting him at his home, I felt, within minutes, that I was with an old friend, and was totally charmed by his good humour, his wit and warmth.

It's quite difficult to be a character in Orkney. There are several to every square metre, but this likeable Londoner has been a character among characters for about 40 years; half of his eventful life.

If anyone else had told me about making his own false teeth from glass-fibre and those flattened segs which were once used to nail boots, I'd have said 'Yes, very amusing.' As Harry Berry described it, it seemed like a handyman's perfectly logical answer to the problem of difficult access to more sophisticated dentistry. Harry has seen and done many things. He's been around a long time, and these stories demonstrate that he hasn't wasted any of it. Humour, keen observation, humanity and compassion, and the natural rhythm and flow of the born story-teller – they're all there. I'll issue a little challenge. Read 'The Driftwood Fiddle', and I defy you not to go on and read the rest.

Jimmie Macgregor.

INTRODUCTION

THESE STORIES OF SEA AND SHORE and cheerful country life were written from the Orkney island of Hoy, Harry Berry's home for the past forty years and more – just over half his life, in fact.

The island has the most varied landscape in the whole Orkney group. To the north, the hills of Hoy rise up, rounded by the long-ago ice, with alpine plants among the stone heights which are reputed to be eagle territory. The island ends in spectacular 1200-foot cliffs which, along with the sea-washed rock column of the Old Man of Hoy, provide one of the great attractions for the traveller on the mailboat *St Ola* that makes the daily crossing of the Pentland Firth. The view compensates for a trip that can at times, with a strong running sea and a northerly gale, require good sea-legs.

Breaking up the heather-covered expanse of the north of the island are just a few crofts and small farms. They shelter under the big hill or hide away in the secluded valley of Rackwick by the sea. Travelling south through the island, however, the level of the land begins to fall, and eventually the road reaches sea level and a more populated area of farms and houses, as it winds its way around headlands and over stone bridges, past piers and fishing slips. On this better farming land, buildings become more substantial, with small villages, farmhouses, and then the stately height of Melsetter House rising up out of a little flurry of trees. Occasionally into the field of view there come less traditional items, pieces of wooden huts and concrete foundations and rusted iron, remnants of wartime and the great Naval base of Scapa Flow.

During World War II, the small township of Lyness in the south of Hoy grew and grew, its dominant feature being the group of oil tanks which supplied the ships. Before the war, Lyness had been the shore base for the great work of salvage of the German Fleet, scuttled in the Flow at the end of the First World War. Once the Second War was over, salvage operations got under way again, although on a smaller scale than before.

Harry Berry had been born in London in the very early years of the century, and had left home at the age of fifteen to join the Navy, where he spent 26 years as a diver. After the War ended he left the Navy – 'with a kitbag, a hammock and nowhere to go.' Being by now married, to an Orkney girl, he decided to try for a job in the islands as a diver working for the firm of Metal Industries on the salvage of the German Fleet.

In the unsettled times that the salvage industry was going through, there was no diving work available, but they offered him a labouring job, and his year's work enabled Harry to buy a piece of land on which he eventually built his home, between Lyness and the neighbouring village of Longhope. When the labouring work ended, Harry was kept on by the firm as a signwriter, giving an outlet to a strong artistic talent. And when Metal Industries eventually ceased operations, it coincided with a vacancy appearing for the post of Customs Officer in Lyness.

So Harry worked as a Customs officer, becoming known to all the islanders and to scores of sea-captains, until after 26 years in the job, the time came to retire again. ('I was one of the Government's bad bargains – I've got *two* long-service pensions.')

He was 'always pretty good with a pencil at school'; and living and working so close to the sea, he developed a great love of painting the sea and ships. The lifeboat service is a cause dear to Harry's heart, and in a community which has a strong tradition of supporting the lifeboat and giving generously to the RNLI, he has painted many pictures of lifeboats and rescues at sea and donated them for fund-raising.

His artistic ability has found many other outlets, including shell novelties, plaster models, and replicas of anglers' trout. But he turned out to have another talent, as a highly gifted story-teller. His tales found their way into print in various magazines, and also onto radio and television, where his broad Cockney accent made him a natural broadcaster. He had a rich source of anecdotes from his varied experiences in the Navy and the Customs service, and from keen observation of the life around him, human and animal. A tale of an unusual pet that appeared in his workshop was selected first for the BBC's *Pick of the Week* and then for the subsequent *Pick of the Year.*

I first met Harry through having the honour to be asked to read one of his stories for Radio Orkney, and subsequently elsewhere. Honesty, humour, and an acute eye for detail are the hallmarks of his work. He stopped writing in the 1980s ('I just dried up') but lives on at his house of Seaview, where there is an ever-open door to visitors and where he cared for his wife in her latter ill-health until she passed on in 1986.

Most of these stories were written to be listened to. Read them with a mental picture of Harry working away on some ploy in his workshop; you are a visitor, a mug of tea in your hand, sitting on a chair beside the stove – watching and listening as he relates each story. There are pauses, clearings of the throat, laughs, asides. So find a comfortable chair, sit back and enjoy them!

Paul Heppleston

NEPTUNE' S BOUNTY
A rollicking yarn of the seashore

IT WAS HORRIBLE. He had almost fainted when he'd touched it. It towered above him, cold, rubbery, slimy, as black as the pre-dawn hour that enveloped it. It was living too. He could hear the slow whistle-like breathing, even though it lay outside the heavily barred cottage door.

It was colossal – as big as the cottage. 'Ebbtide' the beachcomber had risen early, had gone out to empty his slops at the sea's edge and run smack into it. Back indoors, he looked about him. His cottage was packed to its blackened wooden rafters with miscellaneous flotsam and jetsam. Narrow paths led to the bed, window and stove like rabbit tracks through the conglomeration of junk. The walls and ceiling, seasoned with ages of peat smoke, were dark brown, and over everything lay a heavy coat of grime.

The single-wick paraffin lamp on the blackened chest of drawers shone yellow through its dirty glass, and a cheap, loud ticking alarm clock showed the hour to be five; the first light of day, and a very low tide which would have been ideal for the job Ebbtide had had in mind, the gathering of winkles which were numerous along the shore below his cottage.

Ten shillings a bushel – he could have gathered a bushel during the forenoon too; but now that black mountain of something was out there! He reflected that his luck had been good lately – only yesterday he'd found a brand new coil of two-inch white manila rope washed up. It was right there in the room, the whole hundred and twenty fathoms of it, hidden away under the flotsam and jetsam, the ships' furniture, wreckage, junk.

It was becoming lighter every minute, and he decided to have a peep through the little window. Blowing out the lamp, he moved across the room and rubbed a clear circle in the grimy pane with one finger. He peered out; he blinked, still hardly believing what he saw. He shut his eyes, opened them again, but it was still there, almost on his doorstep – Neptune's bounty, waiting to be claimed by him. He shuffled to the door, flung off the heavy oak bar and threw the door wide open. There it lay, alive, all fifty feet of it, brought in by the night tide and stranded – a blue whale!

Ebbtide had been thinking fast. He must secure it to the shore, kill it, then get in touch with the Norwegian whale catchers at their Orkney base on the main island and strike a bargain. This was a big whale. It would make a cargo for at least three of the little whalers, yielding many barrels of oil and tons of beef.

He commenced to move the flotsam and ships' furniture piled around the room and soon uncovered the strong rope which he now felt had been sent by Providence – a hundred and twenty fathoms of manila.

Reaching into the centre of the coil, he grasped the rope's end and backed out of the cottage; the rope, uncoiling like a giant spring, followed him. Throwing the end across the massive body at the tail, he deftly tied a running bowline and heaved the loop taut. He returned to his cottage and, placing a heavy oak beam of driftwood across the inside of the doorway, took the rope round it and hitched it.

The three-foot-thick cottage wall and heavy oak beam would be enough to prevent the animal from drifting off on the rising tide. All that remained now was to kill it and get word to the Norwegians for a buyer.

The telephone was at the laird's house and, come to think of it, the laird would kill the whale too – he liked shooting and killing things. Ebbtide would go straight up to Partridge the head gamekeeper and Partridge would tell the laird – the very thing! But he must hurry, the tide was rising fast.

He left the gamekeeper's lodge much happier, and returned to his cottage. Three neighbouring crofters were standing on the shore, watching two small boys in a flat-bottomed boat who were carving their initials in the whale's hide. He pelted the boys off with stones, ignored the crofters' questions, and flatly refused the help they offered; the laird would be down presently anyway, and *he* wouldn't expect payment for any help he gave. All the laird wanted was to give orders and to be able to shout at everyone, and Ebbtide was quite happy about that so long as the laird didn't want payment for doing it.

'Here's the minister on Titus!' somebody shouted. Ebbtide turned to see the bony thirty-year-old ex-farm Clydesdale coming down the beach on his enormous hooves. In an ancient saddle on his sagging back sat the old minister, rosy-faced, white chop-whiskered, clutching a can of morning milk to his stomach. Titus clopped to a halt.

'Here's the laird!' chorused the crofters. The big shooting-brake skidded to a halt with a deep forward dip on its springs. The laird jumped out.

'Mornin' Padre,' he clipped. Brimming with exuberance he went on, 'Right, let's get started.' He at once became the Colonel again. He was happy, important, in charge of a situation.

'Ebbtide, launch the boat – Partridge, unload the gear,' he commanded. He was supreme, ordering, organising, shouting, exciting himself with his own noise. A pickaxe and coil of rope were thrown out of the brake, and the smallboat was launched. Within minutes he was afloat, surveying the situation.

The tide had risen a full six feet, and the whale, almost waterborne, was lying on its side with the blow-hole just level with the water. As the boat came abreast the massive head, a blast of foul-smelling breath, hissing and bubbling, struck its occupants.

'Poooh!' roared the laird, then added, 'Hey, dammit – the thing's afloat! Put the boat ashore, quick.' Partridge beached the boat.

'Here – clap on here everyone,' yelled the laird, grabbing the manila. 'Heave her till she grounds!'

But fifty-foot whales are not easily moved.

'What about shackling on to Titus?' someone shouted.

'Good idea,' the laird agreed. Partridge produced a rope. The laird pointed at Ebbtide.

'Take a turn round the saddle – then take the bridle.'

'I – I think the whale's coming to life.' The minister's voice came through his cupped hands. Dismounted, he kept at a respectful distance.

The laird quickly hitched the horse's rope to the manila.

'Righto – heave!' he bawled, and gave the horse's rump a hefty smack. The rope tightened like a fiddle string. Titus held the strain for a moment, then the whale, stimulated by the sudden jerk and rising tide, rippled along its entire length, and with a prolonged and loud hissing of escaping breath, rolled over onto an even keel and lay perfectly still again.

Thirty tons of rolling whale was too much for Titus. He was simply hauled back suddenly into a sitting position.

'Hey, Partridge, man the shooting-brake, we'll try a haul with that.' The laird was bursting with importance. They hitched another rope to the bumper, but the combined effort of the now upright Titus and the shooting-brake failed to ground the whale.

'Right,' barked the laird. 'Put me aboard the devil.' The three men manned the small boat and pushed off.

'Gimme the pickaxe, Partridge – I'll deliver the coup de grace.' Ebbtide looked blank at this one.

'Gimme a leg up, Ebbtide – an' I'll knock the blighter for six.' Partridge put the boat alongside the huge body, and the laird, pickaxe over his shoulder, stepped onto the slippery hide just above the tail and walked cautiously forward to the head.

The faithful Partridge, following his master, had tied the boat to the white manila rope, leaving Ebbtide sitting nervously in its stern.

'Killed some things in me time,' the laird roared back over his shoulder to Partridge, who was clutching the great dorsal fin for support.

'Where the devil do these brutes keep their brains?' The laird was standing on the whale's head looking down. He bent closer as if expecting the vital spot to be marked.

'Ah well, we'll give him a smart one between th' eyes, what?' and lifting the pickaxe straight above his head, he poised for a moment, then brought it down with full force towards the whale's skull.

Now it suddenly occurred to the laird, that wielding a twelve-pound pickaxe on a rounded and very slippery surface is not an easy thing to do, especially if one is unaccustomed to wielding a pick; and half way through the arc of the descending axe he found his feet slipping outwards and backwards, with the result that he fell flat on his face, both he and the pick hitting the whale's back simultaneously – full length, the pick penetrating some four inches into the leathery hide.

The whale, now completely waterborne, was shocked into life. It arched itself slowly, as if summoning its strength, then with a colossal heave brought its tail up with such force that the laird's shooting-brake, on the end of the taut rope, was jerked bodily into the sea, its bumper being torn off in the process.

Titus, still tethered by the saddle, happily twisting his thick lips round the sweet grass up at the high-water mark, was rudely jerked into a sitting position for the second time. A little creak of straining leather, a loud *plop* as the straps of the old belly band broke, and the minister's saddle took wings. Another great heave of the whale, a loud twang of the white manila, and Ebbtide's cottage door, complete with its frame and a generous part of the dry stone walls, flew outwards with an explosive clatter.

Ebbtide, stiff with terror, had watched the laird and Partridge slide off the whale's back, seen the brake vault into the sea, the saddle go sailing overhead, his own cottage door become airborne, and now he was moving too – seawards.

In blind panic he threw himself overboard, and found himself shoulder-deep and scrambling for the shore to join the dripping laird and Partridge.

Things were happening up in the cottage, too. The loops of the stiff new manila rope being heaved out of the centre of the coil were springing everywhere, embracing the surrounding junk.

Out of the gaping hole in the cottage wall slithered a grandfather clock, skidding over the pebbles like a coffin, its deep chime jangling as if in protest, followed by a ship's chair, a Victorian whatnot, a whole stream of bits and pieces, each gripped firmly in a loop of rope, and almost at the end – as if to crown the cavalcade, Ebbtide's iron stove, peat sparks showering out of the broken tin fluepipe, rattling and clanking over the pebbles towards the sea, into which it plunged with a loud hiss; and, finally, the bitter end of Ebbtide's new white manila. It seemed to wave them a sad little goodbye before disappearing too with a soft *plip*.

The only thing left in sight was the old boat. They watched it gather speed, towed by the whale into deeper water, and out into the fairway. It was bobbing along at a full fifteen knots as it rounded the point and headed down the channel towards the lighthouse. They watched until the old boat, unable to stand the ever increasing strain – disintegrated.

The lookout in the lamp tower of the lighthouse almost dropped his binoculars; then, after a very long scrutiny, slowly sat down and wiped the sweat off his forehead with the back of his hand. Picking up a pencil, he wrote in the log, very shakily:

10 am. Whale-like monster with rope-like tail over 600 feet long, passed westwards in channel below lighthouse.

Thoughtfully biting the end of the pencil, he studied the entry for a long moment, then added:

balancing a pickaxe on its nose.

He read what he had written at least a score of times; then, slowly shaking his head from side to side, took a rubber, erased what he had written, picked up the telephone and rang for the doctor.

PIPE

YES, I DO LIKE A CIGARETTE, now and again, y'know; but only on Christmas Days and things like that. A pipe? No. Heavens, no, not a pipe! Lor, I only smoked a pipe once and that was over sixty years ago – and it cured me for all time!

It all started in the Gravesend ferry terminal. Y'see, I was in Chatham barracks waiting to join my first ship with a crowd of other boys and we were allowed weekend leave – Friday night to Monday morning. And Chatham to Gravesend was 1/3d return by bus, 24 miles for six new pence! And Gravesend to Southend was 2/6d return – half a crown; that was the ferry included. Over forty miles of travelling for half a crown …

Well, I was with this crowd of boys waiting at the ticket window of the London Midland and Scottish office, y'see, to catch this ferry, and I was third in line waiting for the ticket man to open his little window. Now right beside me, bolted to the wall, was an oak collecting-box – Mission to Seamen thing, y'know. Now in those days a penny was a fair contribution, but I was holding this half-crown between my thumb and my finger and I was dadding it in and out of this collecting-box, y'see, just to make the other boys laugh. And I wasn't looking what I was doing, and somebody leaned along the inside and gave my hand a tap and this half-crown – all I had in the world, almost – shot into this box.

Well, I was left in an awful state, wondering what to do. Of course, all the others had reached the ferry, and I was left all alone. Anyway, one of the Chief Petty Officers came along – one of the boys' instructors – and I told him my story and he lent me half a crown; and I just had time to run for the ferry. And when I got to the Tilbury side, I had to run for the last train. In fact, it was moving when I reached it, and I just managed to get into the last coach.

Now I could see at once that this carriage was full of middle-class snobs. Y'know, professional men that lived in semi-detached places and you could see them having their dinner by candlelight with their little gardens with privets. Anyway, all these men wore pin-striped suits and bowler hats and carried umbrellas – a starchy lot. No doubt these starchy people travelled in the same compartment every day.

And I'd just started to puff at cigarettes, y'know, hand-rolled. I had some tobacco wrapped up in a piece of newspaper in my pocket, so I rolled a fag and lit it. By Jove, that caused an uproar and all these people started fanning themselves with the evening paper and choking and spluttering, and one bossy gent started on at me about smoking. Luckily it was a carriage marked 'Smoking' and I told him so, but he went on about ladies and asking them if I could smoke …

Well, when I got to Southend (my old Dad was alive then) and I told him about it, he suggested I should *really* give them something to complain about!

Anyway, I borrowed one of his doo-dees as they were called – one of those well-blackened clay pipes – and I stuffed it full of black twist. And the next Friday evening I waited and caught the same carriage, purposely, y'see. So when the train started, I got out this doo-dee pipe and lit up. My goodness, there was almost panic in the compartment and everyone was getting on to me.

When I think of it now, I must have been stupid; I'd never puffed a pipe before, let alone a filthy thing filled with black twist. Y'see, I puffed it all right, and gave one big draw and filled my face with smoke. And it tickled my throat so much that I wanted to sneeze. Now when you sneeze, you take in a quick deep breath first; and I did that with my mouth full of this strong acrid smoke and I inhaled the lot. Gosh, I almost died, y'know. The carriage started reeling and I felt violently ill. And I dashed over to the window, which these people had opened in protest, and was sick, with all these middle-class snobs watching me, all the way to the next station, where I got out. Yeh.

It was the last train, so I hitch-hiked a ride in a furniture van drawn by two horses. I was still feeling ill when I got to Southend, three hours later.

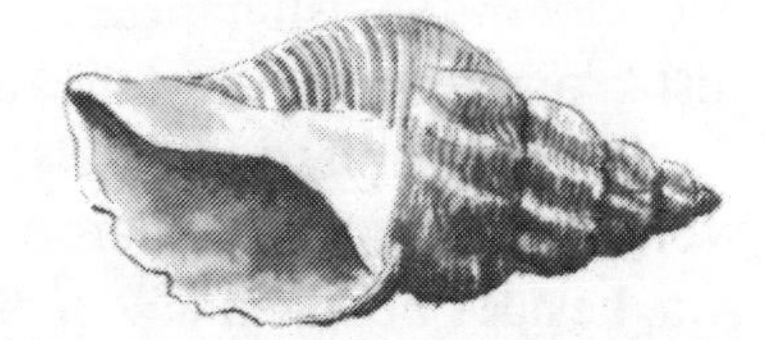

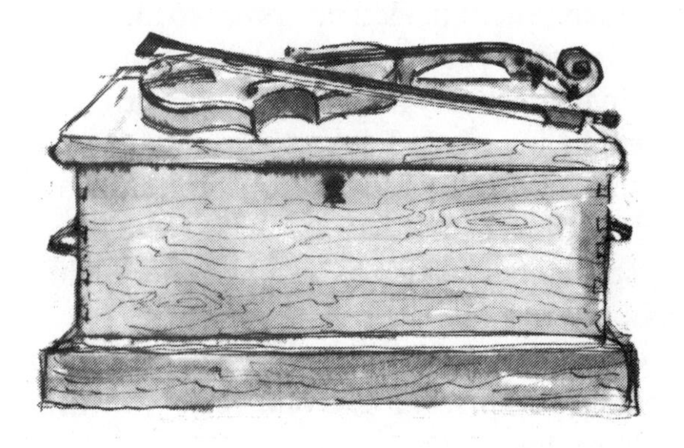

THE DRIFTWOOD FIDDLE

ACROSS THE STRETCH OF HEATHER that separated our houses I had watched him making a pile of the furniture in the little front garden, and somehow I knew that he was going to burn it. He was the only son, and had come north on the death of his mother. His visit would be brief, for he was now a busy man in London; and except for a simple memento or two, he would quickly dispose of the rest of the ancient furniture.

He saw me watching him, cupped his hands and called me across. We both stood before the large confused heap of household effects; old chairs, tables, sofas. He nodded towards the pile.

'I'm burning the lot – it's alive with woodworm!'

For a moment we stood silent, looking at the pile; it was surmounted by the old wooden bed on which he was born, intimate, standing in the garish light of day. Suddenly he said, turning, 'Oh yes, this old trunk, it's full of Dad's tools. I suppose Mother must have put all Dad's things in it after he died.'

He opened the creaking lid and went on, 'I remember *you* had a lot of fun using these tools when you first settled up here - just take anything you want and I'll burn the rest.'

I recognised the tools; I *had* used them in the old man's workshop twenty-five years before. In those days old Sam Dickson, besides being an able member of the lifeboat's crew, was a jobbing carpenter, but his hobby was building small boats into which he incorporated pieces of seasoned driftwood salvaged from the Pentland Firth shore which he combed frequently. I remember the day he picked up the piece of beautifully grained Balkan maple and how, he had told me, he would make a fiddle from it. Eventually he gave up his boatbuilding and devoted all his spare time to the making of his fiddle, and after six months of infinitely careful work it was completed.

I had seen it only the once, when it was finished. It hung above his bench, perfect. The lovely grain of the Balkan maple body, the slender neck of Cuban mahogany, cut from some choice piece of some wrecked ship's furniture, the scroll exquisitely carved, the ebony fingerboard that had once been some mariner's chart ruler – the driftwood fiddle.

We had admired it for a long time in silence, and I could see the old man was immensely proud of his work. Then, unhooking it from the piece of string from which it hung, he laid it against his shoulder as some crofter fiddlers are apt to hold this instrument, and played a reel or two.

I thought it sounded a little harsh, and somehow the old chap seemed to read my thoughts; for he said, very softly,

'I wonder how it would sound in the hands of a master.'

He re-hung it above the bench, and tomorrow he would give the already glass-like varnish its final burnish. But old Sam did not see another day – he died in his sleep that night.

Now I looked down into the chest holding the tools we had both used, badly rusted, with the wooden parts peppered by worm. I lifted them out one by one, laying them reverently in a pile beside the chest; then right on the bottom of the trunk I saw it – the case the old fellow had made to hold his masterpiece.

I gently lifted it out and laid it on the corner of the trunk; the iron snibs broke as I lifted them, the finely powdered dust floated down as I opened the lid, and there before my astonished eyes it lay, as perfect as the day I had last seen it – the driftwood fiddle. The steel strings had long since rusted away and the gut strings hung loose, but the fiddle was untouched, and the flames in the Balkan maple danced as I turned it over in the weak sunlight. For a long time I regarded it with incredulity, then was aware that young Dickson was watching me. I turned my head and our eyes met.

'You keep it,' he said.

If a visitor from the south should enter an Orkney croft where the fiddle is played, not unusually the instrument will be seen hanging against some part of the living-room wall and old Sam used to keep his old fiddle hanging in such a place; so it followed that I took down my best painting and gave the driftwood fiddle this place of honour in my own house. For almost two years it hung there, until I received a letter from an old acquaintance – a concert violinist of some repute, to say that he and a friend would be coming north for a day or two's fishing.

That late August evening is still vivid in my memory. We sat before the red, glowing peat fire in my rather large, lamplit drawing-room, and I told my visitors the story of the fiddle. I'd had the instrument re-strung and my piano tuned, and I asked the violinist to gratify the old man's wish – not that he would hear it, but that I could compare it, for I still remembered how it had sounded twenty-seven years before, harsh and strident; but now I would hear it in the hands of a master.

The elder man, the accompanist, sat at the piano looking through a pile of music for a suitable piece, while the violinist charged the bow with resin, tuned the strings precisely and ran swiftly over some scale. I saw the piece they had chosen was Paganini's Caprice in D Major. Then came the opening bars, the piano soft, the violin sweet, vibrant, alive and infinitely sad, filling the large room with its response to the master's touch.

And then I saw HIM!

Shadowy at first, over there against the softly lamplit wall beside the violinist; now he became gradually clearer until he stood plainly, exactly as I had known him, in his stained white apron, with his white hair, his hands clasped to his chest, his weathered brown face a study of dreamy wistfulness.

Only in some vague way was I aware of the music as it sped on, towards the tempestuous last movement, the violin living, singing, delivering itself of its very soul, the old man watching the fingers of the master as they flew over the keyboard of his creation. And then the last note. As it sadly died away, old Sam turned his head slowly and looked straight at me – smiled once – and was gone.

Until now I have never mentioned my experience to a soul, for after all, it may only have been a figment of my own imagination. Yet sometimes on a winter's night, when the room is bathed in the soft glow of the oil lamps, and the flames in the wood of the fiddle dance as they reflect back the flicker of a peat fire, I fall to wondering, in a whimsical kind of way, what it was that kept the woodworm from it during its dark twenty-five years – and even now, I notice, it never seems to collect the dust …

SIX CUTS

AIRCRAFT CARRIERS?

Yes, I was in some of them in the war. Yes. There was the old *Glorious* – and *Indomitable, Illustrious, Victorious*. They were the carriers that carried the old Buffalo fighters and the dear old Swordfish, y'know, them stringbags with a top speed of 90 knots; just about able to flap their wings to take off with a torpedo. These days, the Navy's different; I saw a bit of a TV film fairly recently about it, chaps tucked up in their bunks (not hammocks), a choice of meals in the cafeteria. There was a rating up before the captain in this film for some serious offence and he jus' got a talking to! There seemed to be something slap-happy about it; I dunno.

The Navy I was in, we were punished for paltry things, silly things. My first punishment in the Navy would, in today's Navy, have earned me the equivalent of a Nobel Joke Award, instead of which the captain ordered my bottom to be smacked – six cuts of the cane; and it was carried out with all ceremony too.

It was early in 1920 and I was sent from the training ship *Ganges* to a light cruiser, one of the split new cruiser squadron; they all carried six-inch guns and they could fire six torpedos in one broadside. And in those days it was a formidable squadron. I suppose a modern guided-missile destroyer today could see five of us off before breakfast, and sink the *Rodney* and *Nelson* as an encore. Yeh, the Navy's changed, right enough.

Well, within a fortnight of my joining this ship, the squadron I was in had to carry out its very first practice shoot – that was twelve rounds a gun. Now the Naval gunnery procedure of 1920 was much the same as in Nelson's Navy – except Nelson used muzzle-loading cannon and World War I ships used breech-loading guns. Communications were the same then too. Nelson used to cup his hands and use megaphones to curse his guns' crews; the 1920 Navy used copper voice-pipes to shout at one another – no electronics in those days at all. Even the cat's whisker set was three or four years away.

Well, in case these copper communications pipes were shot away during an action, each gun had two messenger boys who stood at the rear of the gun, y'see, to rush verbal messages up to the bridge and to rush back again with orders. And I was told to be one of these messengers – for Number Five Gun. The other messenger-boy was a Scots boy with the unlikely name of John Duncan Woodward-Laing. Now Kilty (that's the Scots boy) and I had never heard a gun go off before, and we were excited about it – y'know, watching the gun's crews go through tests and preliminary drill; and suddenly the captain of the gun poked his head around the gun-casing and pointed at me.

'Hey you, bacon-bonce!' (That's a polite Cockney way of calling me a pig's head.)

'Bacon-bonce, go down to the sick-bay and get some cotton wool.'

So I nipped down to the sick-bay and the SBA threw me a melon-sized wad of cotton wool. And then I nipped back up to the gun and gave it to the captain and he handed wads of it all round the gun's crew. And they bunged it in their ears, y'see, 'cause these six-inch guns had a very loud report. Well, he threw the rest of the wool back to me and I stood holding it for a second or two, and then I gave a wad of it to Kilty an' I stuffed some in my own ears – oh yeh, this was great fun!

Ah, but the gun captain, he looked back and he shouted at me –

'Hey you, bacon-bonce, take that wool out of your ears; you're to keep your ears open for orders!'

Well, we pulled the wool out of our ears and I stood looking down at this ball of wool, wondering what to do with it, and the gun captain shouted at me to chuck it overboard.

Now this Number Five Gun was on the after superstructure, y'see, and directly below it was the captain's galley. The captain had his own private galley and chief cook – a Maltese who cooked only for the captain, y'see. And bolted to a stanchion near the ship's side was an open-air meat safe, belonging to the captain; hanging on the side of this safe were two hares. (Y'know, we get a lot of them over in Hoy – they go walloping up the Ward Hill on their elbows.) Well, these two hares were hung there and were beginning to ache … smell … hum … pong. Y'know, the English gentry only eat game when it's high. (They say an Englishman will eat anything, anyway.)

Well, I looked at these hares and I couldn't resist it – and I was holding these four lumps of wool out of my and Kilty's ears, y'see, and I thought that it was a pity to waste it, so I stuffed it in these hares' ears and I looked back at Kilty and pointed and winked, ooh, great stuff, what fun, what a lark we was having, y'see. Well, I chucked the rest of the lump overboard and was just going to take the wool out of these hares' ears when suddenly all hell let loose, y'see – a yelling and shouting of orders and suddenly the gun opened up, twelve rounds of rapid salvos. I just about jumped out of my skin, but it seemed to be over in seconds and I just stood, deafened and choking with cordite smoke. And Kilty and me worked like slaves sponging out the gun, oiling, cleaning, clearing up.

When I was told to fall out, I was only too glad to go to the boys' mess, forgetting all about the wool in the hares' ears. Aaah, but in five minutes a messenger from aft came and yelled out that the Master-at-Arms wanted me on the quarter-deck;

y'see, this Maltese cook had just about took off when he saw these hares' ears bunged up with cotton wool!

Next day I was up in front of the captain on the quarter-deck and he didn't go much on me mucking about with his stinking hares. And he waved me off with six cuts of the cane.

Now I was 16 years old, y'see, and these cuts were given with a great deal of ceremony. Y'see, there was this vaulting-horse, a square, leather-covered box-horse, and it was taken up onto the boys' mess-deck. And the recipient (that was me) wore a clean pair of duck trousers, no shorts underneath, and draped himself over this horse, y'see. There was an officer or two and the boys' inspectors present; and the Jonty (the Master-at-Arms) took up position – he was the one who did the caning – with a cane about three feet long, a solid cane as thick as your finger. That was sixty years ago; I still remember the Jonty clearly, his name was Joyce and he timed those strokes perfectly. He said a jingle as good as a metronome –

'If I wasn't a Jonty, I wouldn't be here,
(Whiiirrrhh......Bang!)
'If I wasn't a Jonty, I wouldn't be here,
(Whiiirrrhh......Bang!)
'If I wasn't...... '

And so it went on, y'see – and after I'd got these six, I got down off the horse and the doctor had a quick look at my sit-me-down and that was that. Y'know, I couldn't sit down for days.

During the dinner-hour that day, all the other boys, being curious, wanted to have a look at the damage, y'see. Well, I wouldn't show them. Y'see, I was so thoroughly ashamed of myself – I was 16 and getting caned like a naughty boy!

Now in that ship the boys had to bath twice a week and that night was bath-night, and y'know, it was a sort of stand-up bath all together; and I tried to hide my bottom with my hands, like a Windmill Theatre fan-dancer. But it was no good, so in the end I let them have a look. And when they saw my stern quarter, they all went Cor! and that made me want to see my BTM for myself. But not being a contortionist, I couldn't get round far enough, so some bright lad suggested a mirror. But the only mirror – six inches square – was bolted to the bulkhead five feet up. And there were no chairs, of course, to stand on; so one boy went down on all fours and I stood on his back and bent forwards and looked through my legs. Y'know, I suddenly felt I was somebody; I was the only one on that ship with those blue stripes.

Now I can't say I used to look forward to those bath-nights – I'd much sooner have been up on deck skylarking about – but that week and the one following, I was first down to the bathroom on bath-nights, sadly watching those blue stripes fading. I was sorry when they'd gone.

Come to think of it, there was a little *romance* in it too; I don't suppose there was ever a man or boy in the Navy that was vain enough to fall in love with a mirror reflection of his own sit-me-down!

Harry was always very fond of animals - especially the ones that people take for granted. And he got much of the inspiration for his writing from the ordinary events of his island life.

He puts these two factors together in this next tale.

HORACE

Y'KNOW, PEOPLE – some people – are concerned about seals, whales and so on, and there are people who make household pets of alligators, snakes and bird-eating spiders. But I've never heard of anyone making a pet of an ordinary slug. Well, not exactly a pet, but being concerned for its welfare, if you see what I mean.

Well, I once had a slug, and I'll tell you how it came about. Y'see, my wife used to keep a cat or two and at night she'd put them out in the shed that joins the house, and there they got their supper and always a large saucer of milk each – y'know, to last them through the night.

Well, one night I was coming in through these back premises and in the torch-beam I saw something dark in the white saucer. So I shone the torch on it, and it was a little slug about an inch long and it was lapping up the milk. Well, I called my wife through and we watched him, y'see, and he had his fill of milk and then he sort of back-pedalled under an old chest of drawers that was lyin' out in these back premises.

He came out every night, all that summer, and he grew into a five-inch monster. Y'know those little horns that stick up, about half an inch long – with eyes on the top of them, I think? I dunno; anyway they stuck out like the antennae on a guided missile destroyer. And sometimes he was waiting for his saucer to arrive and then he'd just lean over the edge on his elbows, sort of thing, and knock back the milk, y'see.

Well, one day in the late summer there came a cold snap and Horace – oh yeh, I called him Horace, dunno why – anyway Horace stopped coming, y'see, because of this cold, and we just said oh well and that was that and we forgot all about him.

Now the winter came in with very heavy rains, so heavy that it came into these back premises, y'see. So I decided to take out the wooden bearers at the base and put down a nine-inch by six-inch concrete sleeper wall. And while I was takin' up the lowest wooden bearer – this rotten bearer, y'see, wooden thing – I saw Horace; and he was sleeping in a sort of cocoon of his own slime, y'know, tucked away for the winter.

Now, he was sleeping just where I wanted to put this concrete wall thing; I know slugs are great escapologists, but it would cramp Horace's style to wake up in the middle of a six-by-nine concrete block, so I picked him up in a trowel with his bed and some earth an' I took him outside to a water tap. I pulled out some grass from the bank and dug a hole and put Horace in, and plugged the hole with the grass again, y'see.

Well, the Spring came and one day I went out to the tap and there was Horace, all five inches of him. So I thought, 'I wonder if he remembers his milk!' So I nipped indoors and got a bottle-top and filled it with milk, y'see, and put it in front of him. Boy, you could almost hear him smack his chops and dive in. I thought, 'You're a bit thin after your winter sleep, Horace, but you're still the biggest slug in Orkney, and I'm going to put some flesh on your bones and make you the biggest slug north of the border.'

But poor old Horace, he only lasted a week after that.

Y'see, I kept a dozen ducks then. They seldom came up the road where the water tap was, but on this one day they did; and one must have got stuck into the bank around the water tap and nabbed hold of Horace. I bet she held him right up by his antennae and quacked, 'Look girls! Look what I've found.' And all the other ducks dived into that bank around the water tap and they stabbed it into a quagmire. But of course, there was only one Horace.

Y'know, that there duck that nabbed Horace – a juicy, five-inch, hand-reared, milk-fed equivalent of a Fanny Craddock dinner – he would have been yum-yum to a duck, eh? Like winning the £5,000 jackpot!

Funny though, the next day I got eight ordinary-sized eggs and one walloper!

But perhaps that was just a coincidence.

THE CAPTAIN'S DOG

IN THE MID–20s I was in a little coal-fired sloop on pirate patrol in the South China Sea, and we carried a passenger that nobody liked – a dog – the captain's dog. It was a cross between a Sealyham – one of those long dogs – and a Scottish terrier, a sort of rough hand-knitted kind of thing, and that dog was certainly cocky – but only when it was near the captain.

On Sunday morning the ship's company would fall in on the quarterdeck for inspection and prayers. We were not allowed to wear shoes on Sunday – the teak deck would be scrubbed and holystoned to banana colour – spotless, and bare feet didn't mark it; the officers wore shoes, of course. Now this dog would follow the captain round inspecting the men, and suddenly it would take a fancy to someone's toes and would let out a shrill little bark and dive at his feet, growling – it never used to actually touch anyone, but if a dog did that to you you'd lift your foot instinctively, and when you'd lifted one foot, he'd make a dive at the foot you still had on the deck, and he'd dive at your feet one after the other till he just about had you running on the spot. Of course, the captain used to shout at him, and stop him, but not before you'd done a ten-yard Olympic sprint.

Another thing this dog would do was to make a run at you and jump up and poke you in the stomach with its nose. I think the dog was only playing – but it would only cut these capers when the captain was close at hand. Y'see, it would pick out someone standing on deck, and would let out a shrill little bark, and its three-inch-long legs would go like Catherine wheels as it charged towards you; then about three feet away it would take off on all fours and jump up and butt you in the stomach.

One day I was kidding the boys on, and told them that the next time the dog made a lunge at them, they should wait until the dog was about six feet away, then suddenly turn round, bend over and look at the dog between their legs; and the dog would be so surprised at seeing a human face suddenly turn upside-down, it would forget what it intended to do in the first place. A couple of days later, the dog thought it would have its fun with *me*. The captain was going up to the bridge – the dog following close, and it gave its usual sharp yap and made straight for me; and some of the boys were standing around on deck watching, so just for fun I thought I'd practise what I'd preached; so I suddenly turned round, bent down, and looked at the dog between my legs.

As usual the dog took off on all fours at once, and I suppose I'd offered it a different target; but by hokey, that dog changed its tactics in mid-air, and instead of butting me – it *bit* me on the bottom, and just stood barking and growling at me. I suppose in its doggy way it was calling me all sorts of things for not playing the game.

Well, a few days after that I was painting rust spots over with red lead under the bridge ladder, and the captain came along the deck and went up the ladder to the bridge, and of course Caractacus … oh yes, that was the dog's name, Caractacus for a little squirt of a dog – that would be a good name for the Loch Ness Monster. Caractacus followed up the first two steps of the ladder, then it stopped and growled and bared its teeth at me; that dog was certainly calling me something.

Y'see, I was sitting on the deck leaning against the iron ladder, and our heads were level and about a foot apart, and out of the corner of my eye I saw the captain move off the ladder top, and at that very moment the dog shot its head forward and yapped shrilly right in my face; in fact, our noses touched. That made me boil with anger, and as the dog turned to go up the ladder, I jabbed the wet red lead brush up under its tail; I think it did the rest of the ladder in one! The captain was right mad about it naturally, and had me up before him on the quarterdeck the next day.

The master-at-arms had made out a charge:

'Able Seaman Berry. Pace forward. Off cap.' Then:

'To the prejudice of good order and naval discipline, Able Seaman Berry did jab one paint brush up the pos—' The captain cut in:

'All right, all right – I know what he did.' He looked me straight in the eye.

'Why did you do that to my dog?' he asked.

(I'd got my defence all worked out.)

'I did it in self-defence, sir.'

'In *self-defence* – !'

'Yessir – the dog flew at me.'

'... It *flew* at you – what, *stern* first?!'

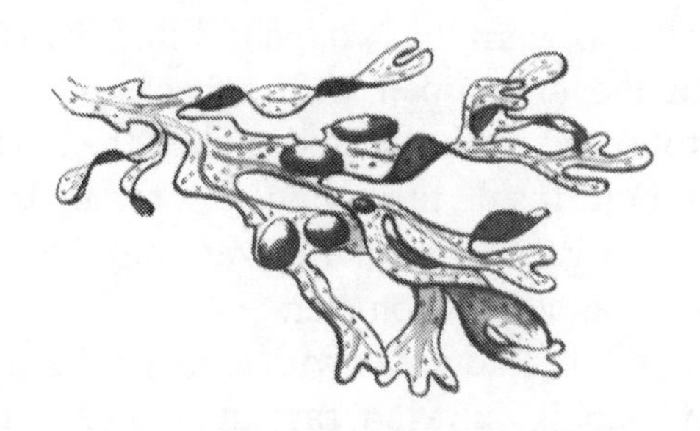

NEPTUNE'S MIRACLE CURE

AT THE AGE OF NINETY YEARS, Angus McTorness has died, a matter of no importance except that it occasions this story, for, as I sit here in the Longhope lifeboat shed looking out over the tumbling foam-flecked water of the Pentland Firth, I recall that stormy night many years ago that we both sat on this same lifeboat locker on which I now write. We were waiting for the return of the Longhope lifeboat, and the old man told me this story. It happened almost seventy years ago.

Angus stood in the stern of the big Orkney yawl, holding up the bunch of fish, a dozen haddocks, held together by a piece of string passing through their gills and out of their mouths, their eyes glazed, staring, their great mouths open wide like nestlings agape. Hamish, standing on the sand and holding the boat's bow, nodded his approval of this gift-to-be.

The others jumped out of the boat and in Indian file the four men proceeded according to mutually understood seniority – Hamish, Sandy, Wally and Angus, tough young lifeboatmen-cum-fishermen, thigh-booted, blue-jerseyed. They sauntered along the clean sand shore in the spring sunshine, to the decaying thatched cottage that stood almost at the calm, sparkling sea's edge. They halted at the weathered, paintless door.

Hamish, without taking his hands from his pockets, turned his back to the door, kicked loudly with his heel on the door bottom as if to warn the occupant, lifted the latch with his elbow, pushed the door open with a backward thrust of his buttock and, followed by the others, entered the ten by four-foot wooden porch built inside the cottage door. Angus, in the rear, hung the fish on a great wire nail driven into the rough boards that supported an ancient barometer.

The large box-like porch with a door at both ends served the purpose of keeping out wind, rain and sea when the door was opened in stormy weather. The four men passed through the heavy teak ship's door of the porch into one of the rooms that comprised the cottage. The dimly-lit apartment was packed to the roof with a conglomeration of flotsam, jetsam and junk. Beneath a small deeply-recessed window of four grimy, cobwebbed panes stood a single iron bedstead.

The fishermen stood in line, silently surveying the occupant of the bed, old Ebbtide the beachcomber, temporarily immobilised with a bout of rheumatism. For almost a minute they stood silent; then,

'Who gave ye *that?'* Hamish nodded at the clean, heavily creased, primrose nightgown the old man was wearing. It looked conspicuous and out of place among the cobwebs and dingy drapings of the bed.

'It's a wumman's too!' Hamish added, bending closer to look at the embroidered neck and lace frills.

Ebbtide gave the four men a hostile stare. He was in no mood for talking, and anyway, a woman's nightgown or not, it was warm and dry, and he rather liked the sweet, sickly smell of camphor it exuded after its forty years of incarceration in one of the laird's trunks of family heirlooms. Besides, after seventy years of bachelorhood he had, only an hour previously, been compelled to suffer the indignity of having his face washed by the bossy younger daughter of the laird. She had made him put on the clean gown and, using a new towel with unnecessary vigour, had left its white fluff clinging to his rudely cropped beard.

'Ye look like an old goat!' Hamish told him. There was a minute's silence.

'Well,' Hamish said with a sigh, 'we've come to see if ye want ony fish.' The old man, lying on his back, head pillowed in his clasped hands, stared up stonily at the blackened wooden ceiling, vindicating his disapproval of Hamish's tactless remarks by refusing to answer. There was, however, a certain satisfaction in being waited on, and on the whole he was rather enjoying it. Taking second thoughts, he said, still staring up,

'Ye can leave some for th' cat.'

' – None for yoursel?'

'Na, the laird's young lassie brings me grub from the big house.'

'Okay – just thought we'd ask, that's all.'

The four men moved to the door and passed out into the box-like porch. A moment later, Hamish stuck his head back into the room and swung in the bunch of haddocks. They hit the stone-flagged floor beside the bed with a squelchy smack.

'S'long, Ebbtide.' Hamish withdrew his head and latched the door.

Outside, the party stood watching the two grey seals, poised on their flippers at the sea's edge below the cottage. In turn, the seals, with all the inquisitiveness of their kind, were watching the four men.

'Fred an' Kate.' Angus nodded towards the shining animals.

' – I bet they miss old Ebbtide!'

'I *bet* they do.'

They watched the seals for some minutes in silence.

'You know what?' Hamish said suddenly, arms folded, thoughtfully chewing a matchstick.

'No – what?' The others were interested.

'Well, them seals are the old man's pets, and if he can't go to them – why not take *them* to him?'

'Yeh, why not? It'll cheer the old boy up!'

'Good idea!'

They fell silent again, each in his mind's eye formulating a plan for the seals' capture; each visualising in his own mind the reunion of the old man and his pets – seeing the seals beside the bed, nuzzling, barking with joy, bringing a ray of sunshine into the gloomy cottage.

'Now, listen.' Hamish held up his hands as a conductor might to command absolute attention. The others listened as Hamish went on.

'They both come up to the high-water mark towards evening, right?' The others agreed; they had watched the seals come looking for the old man ever since he'd taken to his bed.

'Now, they play with Ebbtide 'cause he brought 'em up from pups, but they won't let us get nearer than fifty feet – right?'

'Right!'

'So we wait for low tide this evening, creep up behind the rocks with a seine-net, and cut 'em off from the sea – right?'

'Right!'

'We won't be fast enough!' Sandy objected, with some heat. He went on, 'We might manage to get between them an' the sea, but them seals weigh five hundredweight apiece – we won't stop that weight charging down at us!'

'We'll stop them with the net,' Hamish countered.

'WHAAT! A seine-net – to stop half a ton o' seals charging down like a couple of runaway Clydesdales?'

Hamish saw the sense in the other's argument; he stood, pinching his lower lip for some minutes, then,

'I know!' he brightened. 'We'll slow down their charge!'

'Slow it down – what with?'

'Dogs!'

'Dogs?'

'Dogs; we'll get Ian an' Wallace, Willie an' Jock to bring their sheepdogs!' He became enthusiastic; he added quickly,

'With a wee bit o' luck we might be able to coax 'em right into the cottage.'

The four crofters with their dogs were soon recruited. The prospect of catching a couple of seals delighted them. They crept along, downwind, behind the rocks; the dogs close to heel, bellied down, trembling with excitement, the four fishermen carrying the net, ready.

At the appointed spot, Hamish raised his hand; they stopped. Peeping through the bent-grass they could see the seals, at the expected place fifty feet along the beach, sleek, taut, noses in the air as if sensing the unusual.

Hamish leapt into action; the rest followed with a bound, dogs barking, men shouting, clamorous, whistling the dogs to their stations, all running to cut the seals off from the sea.

The seals, momentarily stupefied, turned and headed down the beach, their velvety bodies humping along in easy, vibrant, shining ripples; the dogs, teeth bared, snapping, yelping, slowed them down while the net, folded in four for greater strength, was run across. One seal, finding a gap at the net bottom, was enmeshed. The noise was now deafening.

'Roll 'im in the net!'

'Call the damn dogs off – gedoff – gedoff – yoop!'

'Get round 'im – lift – lift – *lift!*'

'Up th' beach to the cottage – up – up!'

The original intention of pet and master reunion was suddenly forgotten. Now it had become a challenge; to get the seal into the cottage at all costs. They half-carried, half-dragged the struggling brute up the beach. The cottage door was kicked open with a clatter, and the seal, eight men and four dogs squashed into the porch, barking, heaving, thumping, shouting.

'Out o' the net with him!'

'Open th' door – the bedroom door – open it, open it!'

But the bedroom door could not be opened; it opened *into* the porch and a struggling mass of men, animals and net was jammed against it. The seal, now out of the net, made straight for the daylight.

'Look out! He'll get away – look out – *look out!'*

'Stop 'im – the door – shut it – *shut the door!'*

Somehow the outer door was shut; and now they were in darkness.

The seal began to bellow with ear-shattering volume; the dogs, trodden underfoot, yelped and howled; the men cursed, vociferated; the wooden porch resounded with kicks and thumps. It was bedlam.

Inside the room the old man was petrified. The knuckles showed white as they gripped the grubby patchwork counterpane, hauling it taut up under his nose; his watery blue eyes, wide, filmed, stared out into the piled junk. Only in some vague way was he aware of the awful commotion about him, creating something vast, monstrous, hideous that whirled pell-mell through his imagination.

Inside the dark porch complete chaos reigned. In the confined space the noise was deafening. The three doors were jammed tight shut with the struggling weight of flesh. The wooden walls bulged, splintered, finally exploded into the room, causing the piled junk to avalanche.

The old man suddenly became aware of the growling, solid movement of the piled junk towards the bed. It was too much.

Flinging aside the cover, he grabbed the rusty window catch and heaved. The old window, unopened for years, rotten, came away complete with its frame; he dived into the two-foot-square hole with such force that he came out into the daylight torpedo-fashion, falling flat on his face in the heather.

He was on his feet in a second – a wild-eyed ghost in his ankle-length nightgown. For a brief moment he stood, as if uncertain what to do. Inside the cottage the seal, being first to break out of the wreckage, was just in time to see its foster-parent disappear through the window. It moved fast towards the square of daylight, mounted the bed and dived into the window-opening too. Halfway through it stuck, its fat body plugging the hole and plunging the room into darkness. It was about to wriggle the rest of the way to freedom when it saw its foster-parent only a foot away outside; it roared for help.

The old man had watched it come through the hole in the wall. His blood froze; twelve inches away from his very nose, a great grey, egg-shaped head the size of a bullock's, sticking out of the cottage wall like a monstrous gargoyle, its two massive, bulging, translucent eyes staring straight at him, its thick bristling whiskers twitching – it opened its maw, showing a full set of sharp yellow teeth, then let out an ear-rending bellow.

The old man took off like an Olympic sprint champion.

Titus the ancient ex-farm Clydesdale ambled slowly, sleepily, along the rough road above the cottage, his head drooped, his sagging ears flopping each time his great hooves clopped on the stony road. On his sickle-shaped back sat the white-haired old minister, his side-chop whickers sticking out like teased cotton wool pads beneath the brim of his black homburg hat, his fat jowl and great paunch rising and falling, jelly-like, in time with the beat of the horse's hooves.

Erect, grave, serene, he sat with his eyes shut, meditating on his sermon for the coming Sunday.

Suddenly he became aware of a commotion down by the shore. He reined to a stop and opened his eyes. He could hardly believe what he saw. First, something in a yellow gown legging it along the shore at a remarkable pace towards the laird's house. Then, a seal, popping out of the window-hole like a champagne cork and heading straight into the sea, sending the sea-wrack flying up behind with its flippers in its frantic hurry.

The minister sat for a moment, blinking, peering into the twilight; then, raising and straightening his short fat legs, he brought the heels of his gumboots into Titus's ribs with a smart jab, and jogged him into a shambling trot to the cottage door, just in time to see it open with a crash and spew out a sweating mass of men and dogs. They stopped dead at the sight of the minister and Titus.

'He's gone!' Hamish gasped hoarsely.

'Gone – *who's* gone?' The minister leaned forward in the saddle.

'Ebbtide!'

The minister sat bolt upright, blinked again. Did they mean the old man was dead? He was beginning to feel a little dizzy. His mind flashed back to that work he'd recently read on the transmigration of souls. He'd seen the seal come out of the window and enter the sea with his own eyes! ... Did beach-combers really turn into ...

'There he goes!' A crofter was pointing towards the road that led to the laird's house. Everybody swung round; the unmistakable primrose nightgown was travelling fast over the rough road.

'Stop 'im – after 'im!'

'Bring 'im back!'

The crowd sprang to life. The dogs began to bark, the men to shout, even Titus's limp ears stiffened as he was booted forward by the fat legs; the chase was on – secretly enjoyed by all except Hamish and the minister.

It was dusk. Around the laird's kitchen window that looked out onto the tree-shaded drive, it was almost dark. Jessie Jane, the plump cook, sang in a rich contralto voice as she strained the late dinner cabbage into the sink beneath the open window. She sang into the hot cloud of smelly steam happily, as one who can do something really well and is in the act of doing it. The vibrant notes welling up from her copious bosom froze on her lips. *It* was coming up the drive at a cracking pace. Its shroud, its awful – yellowing – winding-sheet streaming with the speed as it passed the window with a swish; she dropped the pot with a clatter, let out a shattering scream, and hit the floor flat with a sixteen-stone thud.

Ebbtide caught the full blast of the shriek. He doubled his already amazing speed, cleared the six stone steps with a single bound, shot into the hall, into the drawing-room and collapsed in a dead faint in the middle of the floor.

The laird, legs astride, back to the large peat fire, and in the act of drinking a pre-dinner brandy, almost choked. As he heard the clamour coming up the drive, he snatched a fowling-piece from above the great fireplace, loaded both barrels and went to the large French window. He threw it open and waited on the low veranda.

Almost at once the dogs arrived, their number now swelled to eight. They gathered under the window, looking up at the scowling laird, tails wagging, pleased, expectant. Then came Titus, clopping, puffing, bearing the astonished minister; the fishermen, crofters, and some small boys who had joined in, brought up the rear.

'What the devil – !' The laird began recognising the minister.

' – Ebbtide, sir – ' panted Hamish, coming forward.

'Shut up – *you!*' The laird's neck was reddening.

'But Ebbtide – ' put in the other.

'SHUT UP!' The laird was shouting. The minister raised his homburg. Clearing his throat, he said,

' – Er – um – er – if I may – !' He stopped, cleared his throat again, then, ' – Er – um – !' He replaced his hat.

'*You* shut up too!' The laird scowled, chin jutting, and raised the gun.

'Clear off!' he ordered. They backed a step.

'CLEAR OFF!' he bellowed, then fired both barrels into the air.

A hundred roosting rooks in the trees above and around the house, shocked by the sudden loud reports, automatically relieved themselves on the laird and little crowd before taking wing with their strident cries which, mingling with the barking of the dogs, the clopping of Titus, the growling of the men and whooping of the small boys, merged to make a weird cacophony as they retreated at a trot down the drive.

* * * * * * * * * * *

The old minister rearranged his library, keeping only true-blue orthodox books, and Jessie Jane began to attend church with faithful regularity. And Ebbtide? He was completely cured of his rheumatism by his leap into space through his little window, and the little island of Hoy became for a while, even in those times, something of a tourist attraction – to see Ebbtide, the beachcomber, reputed to be the only old-age pensioner to have done the four-minute mile.

CHRISTMAS DOG

IT WAS IN 1924 – Christmas Eve in Chatham dockyard. I was a young AB, one of a party of six Able Seamen and a Petty Officer. We were maintenance on nine World War One minesweepers, rusting old sloops, *Saltburn, Saltash, Magnolia* etc.

One of us had to stay aboard over Christmas, for fire, attention to warps and keeping off unauthorised people and any emergency. I was the only bachelor in the party, so I couldn't help but volunteer to stay aboard for the five days. Everyone was so pleased that they could go home and spend Christmas with their wives and kids that they left me stacked up with Xmas fare – a cold roasted duck, a great chunk of boiled ham, a 5lb leg of roast mutton, and all the other Xmas goodies – oh yes, and a stone gallon jar half full of Navy rum!

Now the crews' quarters in those ships were shocking – exactly like the crews' space in the old steam trawlers; a steep iron ladder from the upper deck leading down to a damp, dark compartment with benches and iron lockers around it, no port-hole, an iron table bolted to the deck and a coal bogey stove on one side – all smelling of bilgewater. There was no electric light.

Well, this Christmas night I sat down this hole surrounded with all this meat and goodies, the only light coming from two thick Navy candles and the glowing red-hot top of the bogey stove. Y'know, Chatham dockyard that night seemed the loneliest place on earth – black – silent – and a four-inch carpet of snow over everything without a footmark in it. But I was down below, warm and happy with a full tummy and a couple of tots of Navy rum, at peace with the world in general. There were no radio sets then in general use, but I was full, mellow and happy, overwhelmed with benevolence and goodwill.

I was looking at the red-hot bogey top and just about to nod off when I thought I saw a movement of the canvas dodger at the top of the ladder – it was pretty dark up there with only the candle light but I saw a thin, animal kind of leg come over the hatch coaming – and it had a lot of little balls on it, yes, a thin skeleton-looking leg with scraggy yellow hair, and these little balls dangling. It looked right weird in the glow of the red-hot bogey top, and then, to my astonishment, another leg came over – and that had little balls dangling from it too. I thought, 'Crikey, it must be the Christmas dockyard ghost – or I've got an attack of the jim-jams – too much turkey and rum – ' Then a thin, whippet-like face poked through the split in the canvas, and it was a dog!

I suppose the poor thing was passing the gangway in the snow and smelt me down below – I mean, it must have smelt something aboard (I don't think it could have smelt *me* from the dockyard wall – I didn't smell that bad – not in those days, anyway). Well, there it was, at the top of the ladder. It stood there for a full two minutes, no doubt waiting for me to chuck a boot at it, but I didn't. I suppose the poor thing knew I wasn't going to hurt it, so it all came over the coaming of the hatch, and stood trembling on the top step. Then it came slowly down the ladder – a yellow, scraggy, whippet-like affair – tail between its legs, and the little balls on its legs were balls of ice where its hair had been dragging through the snow.

It stood trembling in front of the hot bogey stove – gosh, it was the thinnest dog I've ever seen – its bones were sticking out – its ribs – it reminded me of a birdcage, and the poor creature stood looking up at me, sort of bewilderment in its eyes. It didn't seem to believe that a human being could show it kindness and give it warmth and shelter – it couldn't believe its senses.

I was so overcome by compassion that tears ran down my face, and I'm sure there were tears in the dog's eyes too; I turned, very slowly so as not to alarm the dog, and reached into the iron locker where the Christmas goodies were kept and lifted out the 5lb leg of cold roast mutton, and gently put it down in front of the dog.

Y'know, the dog just looked at it; I would have thought the dog would have sniffed it – then smacked its chops and start to yog into it. But it didn't. It just stood looking down at it for fully half a minute; then it looked up into my face – and keeled over in a dead faint – the poor brute couldn't believe its eyes either!

QUIRKS OF A MESSMATE

I WAS ONCE on a ship with a real character – an all-round funny chap. I remember he had a gramophone, one of the first portable ones – y'know those things; before that the gramophones had a big trumpet on, y'see, but this of course was in 1925.

And he only had one record for this thing, but I remember it well; on one side it had *The Drinking Song* from *'The Student Prince'*, y'know, and on the other side was that market thing – what's it called now, all curry and rice music – oh yeh, *In a Persian Market,* that's it. And he played this record a coupla times every night and of course it just about wore out. It was just about the time that radio sets were coming into being, but they didn't get as far as the South China Seas.

He used to eat onions too – raw. He'd eat them like apples.

In those days there was no cafeteria messing – every mess did its own cooking, and used to have its own vegetable locker at the end of the mess table. At nights the boys would be at the mess table playing cards or writing, but this fella, he'd get up and he'd go along to this vegetable locker and he'd take out a big Spanish onion, and he'd sit at the back of the table and he'd take off the outer skin of the thing and he'd start munching it. And, d'you know, it never used to make his eyes water. Everyone else at the mess table used to start crying, but not him!

Yes, and another thing he used to do was to drink Seidlitz powders in an unusual way. These Seidlitz powders – I don't know if you've ever tasted them – but they were good if you had a hangover; sort of effervescing things, like liver salts, y'see. And they cost a penny each and came in a grey packet and inside this there were two other packets containing the powders – one in white and one in blue. What you do is to mix these two powders separately in cups, y'see,and then you pour one cup into the other and you get a sort of explosion of effervescence, y'see. You had to wait until it settled down, of course, because it was pretty powerful stuff. You couldn't drink it as it was fizzing, because it would get up your nose and make you sneeze.

But this chap used to mix the two cups and then he'd drink one cup and then he'd smack his chops and then he'd drink the other cup. And he'd shut his mouth and hold his breath and this chemical reaction used to take place inside him, y'see.

Y'know, you could see his eyes really sparkle! And after about half a minute he'd open his mouth wide and, d'you know, you could hear him all over the ship, because he came out with the loudest burp you've ever heard!

ROUGH JUSTICE

IT HAPPENED at the turn of the century; the missing man had been washed up, and the coroner's verdict was 'death by misadventure'. And in a way that was right, he *had* fallen from the cliff-top; but old McTaggart was the only living person that knew the full story, and after seventy years' silence he confided in me.

Old David the shepherd sat on a mossy sandstone ledge. From the contents of a crumpled paper bag, cupped in one horny palm, he made his midday meal of goatsmilk cheese and coarse oatcake which he munched slowly on strong teeth. His skin, in contrast to his wiry white hair, was tanned to the semblance of leather and deeply wrinkled, and his keen blue eyes looked out of slits in his expressionless face. This was his favourite seat; for sixty years, since boyhood, he had tended the laird's flock of ewes at lambing time up here on the plateau. From where he now sat, taking his morsel of food, he could look plumb down the cliff-face to the sea far below.

His gaze was fixed on two of the sheep which had jumped down on to a ledge of the cliff-face and were cropping at the sweet grass that had tempted them down. They were ten feet below him, separated from him by a forty-foot-wide chasm that gashed back some hundreds of yards inland, its perpendicular walls dropping a sheer thousand feet into the sparkling, foam-flecked water.

The old man's gaze wandered along the ledge to where it narrowed suddenly to some twelve inches, then a dozen feet further along to another, wider part – and the eagle's eyrie, built under an enormous overhang of the sandstone cliff.

For more years than he cared to remember, successive pairs of eagles had used that ledge for their nest. Here they would stay for some twelve weeks; then they would go, leaving the youngster to fend for itself.

The old shepherd remembered, too, how he had gone down each year to the abandoned nest, along that dozen feet of narrow ledge to see the conglomeration of fur and bones they had left, sometimes the rings of long-distance racing pigeons,and often the dead eaglet, thrown from the nest by the stronger chick and ignored by the parent birds. He looked at the narrow ledge along which he used to go, arms outstretched, face flat against the rock, feet pointing opposite ways, shuffling, inch by inch. He had not been there for a good many years now, but he always looked forward to the eagles, to see them arrive each lambing time; and somehow, he reflected, they did not seem to mind him being about – they were indeed his friends. His mind went back to the present pair's arrival – a fortnight ago, on top of this very cliff, he'd watched their mating, and now two eggs would be in the nest.

The old man's thoughts turned to the strange visitor who'd surveyed the ledge through binoculars for most of yesterday afternoon. The fellow could not see the eyrie, but he knew it was somewhere along that ledge. Nobody had done that before. People very seldom came up here on the moor, the shepherd reflected. Sometimes it was weeks before he saw a soul, but this stranger ... There could only be one reason; collectors would give a great deal for golden eagle eggs, and the ledge he was now watching held the only pair of eagles in the northern isles. But the ledge was narrow, and that enormous overhang would preclude any rope lowering-- and the eagles might even attack a man on that narrow ledge.

Beneath his weathered leathery skin, the old man smiled at his own reflections. He seldom smiled, and even when he did it barely showed; his puckered face was incapable of expression.

Suddenly his keen eyes saw a figure top the rise in the moor about a mile distant – the stranger! The shepherd sat perfectly still – just as the wild creatures of the moor with whom he was familiar evaded detection – until the approaching figure dipped into a fold of the ground. The old man lay down and belly-crawled to the edge of the sheer cliff face. From this position he could look in towards the ledge across the deep chasm, forty feet away. Somehow he knew the stranger was going to make an attempt at the eyrie. He wondered what would happen on that narrow ledge – but whatever happened, he would be in a position to see, without being seen. A thousand feet below him he could see a thousand birds; the ravens, soaring and rolling, the kestrels and falcons sporting in the up-current of air along the cliff face, the comical puffins skimming and splashing over the tumbling water. He lay, chin on clasped hands, behind a heather clump – perfectly still.

Carrying a large knapsack, the man arrived. For some minutes he stood looking down at the ledge. The small dog he had brought with him yapped incessantly. Leaving the dog, the man slipped down onto the sheep track, emptied the contents of the bag and assembled the butt and barrels of a gun, which he loaded.

The eagles, disturbed, soared from the eyrie into space. Laying down the gun, the man walked to the end of the wide ledge under the overhang and surveyed the twelve feet of narrow track. The dog, afraid to jump down, ran back and forth yapping shrilly.

The eagles, soaring in a wide circle above, saw the man disappear under the overhang – they would not attack a man, but they were more than a match for a small dog. The female bird hung for a moment, then stooped toward the dog; but the dog, sensing rather than seeing the shadow of the great bird as it struck, rolled, howling with terror as the raking claws and slashing beak missed. The man, shocked into action by the dog's scream, grabbed the gun. The eagle, bent on knuckling the dog down, turned in a tight circle, making a perfect target for the man. The male bird, circling above, could not see the man but only his mate as she crumpled in mid-air, her torn wings flailing as she dropped. His instinct told him she was in her death plunge; he plummeted down with her, stooping with her tumbling body, calling his pathetic *twee-o, twee-o.*

The old man saw the golden body hit the water and float very still while the male circled it close, calling piteously. It seemed a long time before the eagle stopped circling his mate. Then in a great sweep the old man saw him rise, the primary feathers splayed like fingers, beating the calm air as he soared up the cliff face on the thermal current – upward, upward, with talons ready to strike, the hooked beak ready to slash, the head turned sideways, seeking above for the creatures that could kill with such violence and swiftness.

The eagle saw his quarry, the dog, still close to the cliff face. He cartwheeled over with a magnificent show of spread wings, then stroked powerfully down; in one slashing welter of blood and bestial fury, it was over.

Exhausted, the eagle drifted out over the cliff face. Too late he saw the two close-set, round, black, steel-rimmed eyes looking straight at him. He saw them light up a brilliant blue, but he did not hear the report as both barrels barked.

The shepherd watched the great bird go down the face, gently striking the protruding rocks, the golden-brown feathers bursting from the twisting body in little flurries each time it struck. He watched it hit the water near its mate. His deeply-lined face was expressionless, his mouth a hairline, his eyes the merest slits. He did not move.

He watched the man lay down the gun, then cross quickly to the narrow ledge. Flattening his body against the rockface, the man inched cautiously along towards the eyrie and the two still warm eggs.

He was a little past the middle of the ledge when it happened – just as the old shepherd expected; some five feet of the ledge, just crossed, dropped into space. The man, his ear against the rock, stopped, listening intently for the very faint sound that was transmitted through the rock. For fully a minute he stood, as if crucified to the face, unaware that his left toe was but an inch from a thousand-foot sheer drop. Summoning courage, he turned his head. Then, through the gap of his left arm and the rockface, he saw it – that vast drop. He froze, staring at the gun only six feet away, the pale sun glinting on its blued-steel parts, lying there on the solid part of the ledge – and between, that hideous space.

He began to tremble, sucking his breath in great gulps, the knuckles showing white as he gripped the sandstone face, unable to move, rigid, terror-struck.

Slowly the old man got to his feet. The other, catching the movement above him from the corner of his eye, turned his head. 'Hey, you,' he panted.'Get help quick – *quick*, I say.'

The shepherd stood quite still. The man shouted: 'Get help, I say – get a plank – that's it, a plank – ' He stopped for a second, then:

'Yes – a plank – you can lay it – '

Again he stopped. He looked up into the old man's face, the eyes and mouth the barest slits – an Indian's face, expressionless.

'D'you hear me!' the man almost screamed.'Get help – get – get – !'

He stopped; something seemed to tell him the old man did not intend to help him. He could feel those eyes through the slits burning into him. The shepherd stood perfectly still, as if carved from the very sandstone on which he stood, silent – inexorable. The man on the ledge, arms outstretched, fingers hooked, trembled with fear. That strange hypnotic feeling that precedes sleep came upon him, and in that instant he knew he was going to faint. The rockface receded from him, swallowed in a purple void, the outstretched arms dropped, the knees buckled, and the man on the ledge went down.

The old shepherd watched the tumbling body on its long drop. He watched it hit the water close to the still floating eagles, and sink into the gin-clear sea. Then he turned and slowly walked back to his lambs.

LAMP-POST

IN 1930 I was in a little ship surveying in the South Pacific,and once we had to go down to Invercargill – New Zealand – right at the southern tip of the South Island to pick up a scientist who'd been on the Antarctic icecap for some time.

We were there just one night, and me an' a coupla shipmates decided to go ashore for a coupla hours an' a glass or two o' beer. Blimey – it turned out to be a night to remember. It's a sordid story, but it 'appened fifty-three years ago, so I s'pose I can tell it. Well, being three young fellas, we had quite a few beers, and before goin' back to the ship we decided to have something to eat, and we called in at a pub on the waterfront. It was a long narrow bar, an' the place was empty except for a bartender – a big fellow in a white apron who stood under a single light, polishing glasses – the rest of the bar was in darkness.

Now against the bar stood a long row of high stools,'cause it was the kind of pub where you could get a cooked snack at the bar, so we sat up on these stools an' ordered three beers an' three plates of fried oysters. The bartender served up the beers, an' shouted our oyster order through a little trap-hatch, then he carried on with his glass polishing. He was one of those characters that always seem to have a scowl on their face, an' for some reason he stared at me; an' me, having nothing to do except wait for the fried oysters, stared back at him. My two shipmates – one either side of me – laid their arms on the bar top an' rested their heads on them, facing me an' the bartender having this staring match.

Now on this bar top, spaced along it for decoration, were little glass flower bowls, each with three or four chrysanthemums – white pompom sort – an' one bowl was right in front of me. Now we'd been staring at each other for fully two minutes, all the time he was picking up and polishing glasses without taking his eyes off me, so I thought I'd give him a sudden surprise; an' without lookin' down, I took a chrysanthemum from the flower bowl, dipped it in the salt, an' ate it. His face just stayed wooden. He just kept polishing glasses, so I took another – in fact, I ate the four chrysanths in the bowl.

He gave me time to swallow the last flower, then he took the empty bowl away, reached out along the bar, an' pushed another bowl of chrysanths in front of me, an' carried on with his glass polishing, never takin' his eyes off me face. I'd had enough of chrysanths, so I rubbed me tummy an' made a sort of family way sign, meaning I was full up. Then he stopped his polishing, an' leaned across the bar on one elbow.

'Sailor,' he said, 'I've met a lot of queer fish in me time – but you're the first chrysanthemum eater I've ever met.'

I said, 'Is that right?'

'Yyy-up,' he said, 'you're unique, sailor – as unique as that lamp-post outside.'

I said, 'An' what's so special about that lamp-post outside?'

'Well,' he said, 'It happens to be the most southerly lamp-post in the British Empire.'

When he said that my ears shot up like Mr Spock's, and the three of us nipped outside to have a look at it – can't remember if it was oil or gas or electric – anyway, the three of us stood round it.

I thought it was an opportunity too good to miss – the street was dark and empty, so I unbuttoned me flaps an' started to spring a leak against it – just for the heck of it, I s'pose. I'd hardly started when I was grabbed by the scruff of the neck by two big bobbies who'd been watching from a corner. They marched me down the road to the copper-shop and I struggled violently. These bobbies held me all the tighter – they thought I was strugglin' to get free; but I was strugglin' to get an arm loose, 'cause they'd grabbed me so quick me privvy member was still hangin' out!

The desk sergeant was very good – I s'pose he could see the funny side of it. He knew we were sailing in the morning, so he fined me on the spot – five bob! Y'know, I've never regretted paying that five bob. I bet there are a lot of fellas who would be only be too happy to pay twenty-five pence for the privilege of springing a leak against the most southerly lamp-post in the British Empire, eh?

ERNEST

ONE AUTUMN DAY I decided to pay a quick visit to Hoy, for I hadn't been there for a long while, and I took the opportunity to drop in on Harry. That afternoon, with an hour to spare before the ferry home, I sat in his workshop as the wind rustled the long-dead grasses outside the window. We got talking – about animals, pets, wildlife and so on – and Harry asked me if he'd ever told me the story of Ernest.

'No,' I said. 'What kind of animal was Ernest, Harry?'

'A spider.'

'A special one, perhaps?' I ventured.

'Yes,' replied Harry. 'Very.'

I suppose Ernest the spider gave me more pleasure than any other creature, perhaps because I was able to watch him all day for some months. Y'see, I met him early one summer morning; I was going into my workshop and just before I grabbed the door- handle, I noticed a tiny spider web spun from the handle to the door-frame. Now – I never break a spider's web, if I can avoid it of course. But I had to get into my workshop, so I swept my finger round the web, pickin' it up together with the tiny spider. Oh, 'e was just about as big as a match-head, y'know – a very small thing – and I took it round to a south-facing window where the bluebottles and other flies sun themselves during the summer.

Now this little spider must have liked the new position, for in an hour or so it had spun another three-inch web, right up in the corner, y'see, of this window.

Well, he stayed there all the summer. 'Is web grew bigger and bigger until it filled a three-foot by eighteen-inch window and he'd grown into an enormous fella – of course on a plentiful supply of flies, y'see. I called him Ernest because he was so – what's the word? – *meticulous* about his web. At evening, his web would be torn to bits with his daily battle with the bluebottles, but the next morning it would be mended and perfect.

But it was one late summer morning I went out and I saw his web hanging in tatters. I went outside and looked in his hidey-hole, but he wasn't there, so I looked below the window; after all, he was the spidery equivalent of the Fat Boy of Peckham and might have dropped dead with a fatty heart, but I couldn't see him anywhere. And I was thinking about him all morning and it struck me that it might be the spiders' mating time – and that Ernest had taken himself off, perhaps to find a lady friend.

Now that cheered me up, y'see, and I felt very happy for him and I hoped that when he'd done what he thought he had to do, if you see what I mean, he'd come back.

Well, I was thinking about him and it suddenly occurred to me that somewhere I'd heard that after the spidery nuptials, the lady spider promptly makes a meal of the gentleman spider, for um, y'know, services rendered – so to speak. By hokey, I thought, that's not going to be so good for poor old Ernest; but I thought, Ernest is a big fella and he'll be able to take care of himself if it comes to a roughhouse. I thought: 'He'll be back, all right.'

But that evening I had a visit from a fellow that comes up each year for the trout fishing – Andy Reid: he's a keen expert with the rod. Well, he came into my workshop holding the fattest trout I'd ever seen, a three-pound beauty! And being an angler myself, I asked him what fly he'd taken him on. He said he'd come along to my workshop earlier that day to ask what fly he should use up on the loch, but I wasn't in.

And then he horrified me.

He said: 'I was just leaving the workshop when I noticed a dirty big spider outside your window, so I popped him in a matchbox, and that's what I caught the trout on.'

I looked at him speechless for a couple of seconds. 'Andy,' I said, 'that wasn't a dirty big spider; that was Ernest and Ernest was a friend of the family.' Of course, Andy was very upset about it and he offered me the trout he'd caught with Ernest, yes.

Harry was thoughtful for a while, looking out of the window, and I guessed he really had been pretty fond of that spider. Eventually I asked him, 'Did you take it?'

'How could you!' he exclaimed, turning towards me with a hint of the accuser in his voice.

'Well, after all, it would have been some kind of recompense.'

'Look, if I'd cooked and eaten that trout, thinking of Ernest, I'd have suffered from dyspepsia for the rest of my life!'

 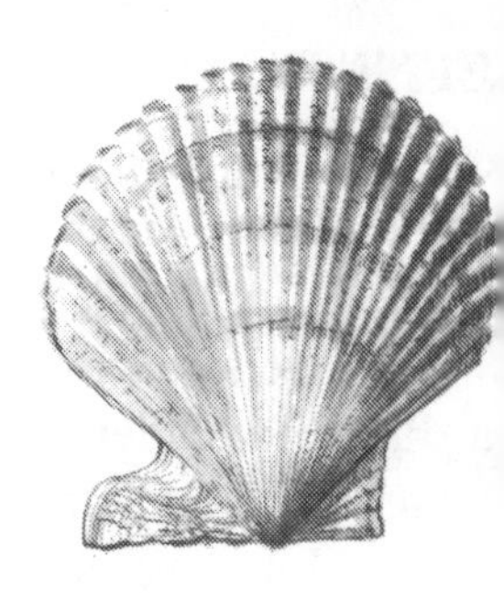

FOOTBALL FISH

OF ALL THE ARTISTIC things I'm asked to do, copying fish is my favourite. When the anglers over in the mainland lochs land a really big one – five, six or seven pounds – they sometimes send them over to be copied and I've made a study of fish, their anatomy and markings (it's surprising that a man can know so much about fish without being able to catch the darn things). I like eating fish too, I could live entirely on fish; once I even ate a football fish – well, we used to call them football fish.

You see, in 1931 I was out in the South Pacific on a little Navy sloop surveying the island groups, and we used to anchor inside the coral reefs at night. And the reefs were teeming with brightly-coloured fish – multi-coloured – black and yellow stripes, blue and gold, red and yellow, purple and silver, different varieties and species; and we simply called them football fish – because they looked as though they were wearing football jerseys. We didn't eat them; they were supposed to be poisonous. They weren't, of course, but nobody would think of eating a football fish.

This little ship I was on had a closet-sized refrigerator that could take three or four sides of beef – there was no room for frozen fish, so once we'd left Auckland we'd tasted our last fish for two or three months. This might suit some people, but I missed fish very much. Every evening the men used to catch these football fish, just to pass the time away; they would just unhook them and throw them back into the sea. I was passing through the well-deck one evening and a laddie hoisted a football fish on to the deck. He unhooked it and was about to throw it back when I said,

'Hold on – I'll take it.' He held the fish out to me.

'What are you going to do with it?' he asked.

'I'm gonna eat it! '

I don't think he believed me. I don't know what made me make up my mind on the spur of the moment; perhaps it was because it wasn't so highly coloured as most of the reef fish. It was a blue and silver striped thing of about a pound weight.

Within a minute of me taking that fish, every man in the ship knew that Harry Berry was going to eat a football fish.

The galley on that ship was amidships on the upper deck, about ten feet by six, and it had two big stable-type iron doors on each side, the top and bottom half opening independently. Within a minute or two of me taking that fish into the galley, most of the ship's company had gathered round the open doors watching me fillet and skin it. I was sickened by the look of it; it was a dark flesh – like a coalfish with a thin, transparent look. But I had an audience and I wasn't going to give up now; I fried it and put it on a plate.

The boys never spoke a word. They opened the galley door and made a gangway for me; they fell in behind me and followed me for'ard to the messdeck hatchway. I went below, put the plate on the scrubbed table and sat down. The boys dashed to the mess-shelf and got a knife and fork, salt, bread, margarine, vinegar and a cup of cold tea. Then they sat on the opposite mess-stool, folded their arms on the table, and all the rest stood at the rear and all around me, and nobody said a single word.

I picked up the knife and fork, stood, and bowed all round, then I sat down and began to nosh that fish. By hokey – it tasted revolting, but I pushed it down, sometimes smiling all round, trying to let them see I was enjoying it. (I think they were all waiting for me to drop dead.) But I got it down and put down the knife and fork. The boy opposite me on the mess-stool held up one hand and pointed to a tiny morsel I had left – about the size of a couple of match-heads, so I picked it up daintily on the end of the knife and put it on the tip of my tongue. The boys then gave me a standing ovation – it could be heard all over the ship.

I stood and bowed deeply all round – then suddenly I felt violently ill. I vaulted over the table, up the ladder and to the ship's side and was thoroughly sick; I threw up every mortal thing in my stomach. I'll say this for the boys – they let me be sick in private!

That put me off eating fish for a time, but I soon got back to enjoying it again; and now, I'll eat any fish – except perhaps mackerel – probably because it's blue and silver.

THE SHOW-OFF

IN THE EARLY THIRTIES I came home in a ship that had been surveying in the South Pacific for two years, and while in New Zealand I'd learned to drive a car; so I bought myself a second-hand little sports car to scoot around in on my long leave. I thought I would drive down to Exmouth in Devon to see my sister, so I left Southend-on-Sea one morning – dressed in uniform – bluejacket's clothes (I was always a bit of a show-off and it was a novelty in those days to see a bluejacket driving a car).

I had to cross London to get to the West Country and got as far as some main crossroads in Whitechapel, East London, in a line of traffic that had been stopped by the traffic bobbies. I can't remember if traffic lights were fitted there at that time, but police were directing traffic on that day, anyway. I was in front of a line of vehicles, some horse-drawn, and I wanted to turn left.

In New Zealand, at that time, a driver could filter to the left even though his line of traffic was stopped, so thinking it was the same over here I started to filter. At once a shrill police whistle brought everything to a stop. Everyone was looking round to see what had happened.

Then I saw this big police sergeant walking towards me – slowly with the full dignity of the Law! He stopped about six feet away; he didn't say anything – just stood looking for about fifteen seconds, then he put his white gloved hands behind his back and walked slowly right round my little car. He stopped at the licence holder and held his head right over on one side to read it. It was one of those old-fashioned round iron holders, sticking out from the windscreen on an inch strap of iron, with a round glass window that was screwed on. It was extremely difficult to get the licence upright, for when the glass touched it, it would screw round with the glass – and mine was on its side.

He came slowly round to me, and by this time all the motors were honking their horns and the Foden steam wagons rasping their klaxon horns, ringing their bells and blowing their whistles – it was bedlam; but this sergeant took no notice. He said,

'An' where did you think you was goin', sailor?'

I thought, 'Well, I'm in for it now anyway,' so as naive as I could I said, 'I was goin' to see me sister in Devon.'

This bobby looked at me as much as to say 'By hokey, I've got a right one 'ere.' After a second or two he shot out his hand – straight out, and I really thought he wanted to shake hands with me; I was about to take his hand when he withdrew it, leaned down and shouted:

'Driving licence!' I just about jumped out of the car. He read my licence, accepted my excuse for filtering, then:

'All right, sailor – carry on and see your sister!'

I was just going to move off when he held up his hand and stopped me.

'That licence, sailor – get it the right way up.'

With all the traffic impatiently hooting their horns and sounding their whistles and klaxons I was beginning to feel impatient and angry myself, since I was the cause of the hold-up, so I said, tartly, 'Well – you can read the thing, can't you?'

He walked the few paces back to the car, more slowly than before, bent forward with his hands on his knees till our faces were about six inches apart.

'Sailor – I'm a policeman – not an acrobat – I'm not expected to do a bliddy handstand to read people's licences!'

NEPTUNE'S FERRETS

IT was the quick trained eye of Partridge the gamekeeper that spotted him as he topped the rise in the heather moor just ahead.

'Here comes that old goat Ebbtide, sir!' he barked.

The laird of Hoy and his woman guest, guns under arms, returning from the morning shoot, stopped and watched the old man as he shuffled along the track towards them.

'Who's Ebbtide?' the woman in tweeds asked.

The laird watched the approaching figure for a moment, then with a sympathetic note in his voice,

'Oh, he's an old fellow – a beachcomber; he lives down by the shore.'

The laird's face softened. He went on,

'He's a harmless, simple old man' – he glanced at the keeper – 'Partridge here dislikes him very much.'

The keeper's face hardened; he put in quickly,

'He's a cunning old goat – him, and his Neptune's ferrets!'

The woman looked at the laird; perplexed, she asked,

'Did he say Neptune's ferrets?'

The laird, still watching the old man's approach, laughed.

'Oh yes, Neptune's ferrets – you'll see for yourself in a moment. Here he is.'

Ebbtide came to a halt some six paces from the party. He stood as if overawed by the presence of the laird and the woman, head lowered, his watery blue eyes looking up from under the brim of his battered homburg, his unshaven face pinched and sad, and his sparse frame enveloped in an enormous old overcoat turned up at the sleeves. From his left hand hung a bright tin by a string handle.

'Hello, Ebbtide – going ferretin'?' The laird's voice was kind.

The other nodded quickly.

'Show us what you've got in your tin!'

Ebbtide raised the tin at arm's length. The laird stepped forward and looked in.

'Ah, four of 'em, eh?'

The woman, overcome by curiosity, moved forward and peered into the tin; then, lifting her gaze to the beachcomber's face, she said,

'Good Heavens! – little green crabs!'

'Show 'em the rest of your jiggery-pokery,' snapped the keeper.

The woman shot a resentful glance at the speaker. She had been in his company for only three hours – and disliked him intensely; his self-assurance, his cockiness, his strident reiteration irritated her. She had not enjoyed the morning's shoot.

'Go on – show 'em the rest of your hocus-pocus!' the keeper rasped.

The old man returned the keeper's hostile stare with a childlike smile, then dived his right hand deep into his overcoat pocket, rummaged around and brought out a clenched fist, extended it to arm's length and slowly opened it. In his palm were four one-inch lengths of charred candle and a small ball of soft putty. The woman, more perplexed than ever, looked at the odd assortment. Turning to the laird, she asked, incredulously,

'What on earth does he do with those?'

The laird smiled at the old man. Gently he said,

'Ebbtide, show us how to make a Neptune's ferret!'

Then, explaining the old man's actions, he went on:

'You see, he takes a little green crab from his tin, then a small ball of putty which he sticks on the crab's back; then on to the putty he sticks a short piece of candle – and there's a Neptune's ferret! Now all he has to do is light the candle and pop the crab into a rabbit burrow, and when the rabbits see the light moving towards them – they bolt!'

The laird smiled at the beachcomber and added, as if to close the discourse,

'Hope you get a rabbit today, Ebbtide.'

The old man grinned, nodded quickly and backed away, then he turned and scuffed off in the direction from which the party had come. They watched the receding figure for fully a minute in silence – the faded green overcoat that covered the bent back, the frayed trousers, the heavy hobnail boots and the bright tin he carried so carefully. The woman, eyes brimming with tears, said, very softly,

'Oh, the poor old man!'

The party resumed walking, then the laird began in a reminiscent tone:

'I met the old fellow down along the shore one day when I was out after a duck or two; he was gathering winkles. He picked up one of the shore crabs from under a rock and explained his ferret idea, and I was so tickled by it that I gave him permission to try for a rabbit whenever he liked. Of course, he knows Partridge here will not allow any form of snaring, trapping, coursing or ferreting on the estate – but even Partridge could hardly refuse to let the old chap try with his crabs!'

A sarcastic note came into the laird's voice as he added,

'Partridge boasts that not a single grouse, hare or rabbit falls victim to a poacher on this estate – that right, Partridge?'

The gamekeeper jumped at the question with:

'No sir – nobody! Poachers would have to be pretty fly to catch me!'

The woman winced at the last remark. She said to the laird,

'But this Neptune's ferret idea – does it really work?'

The laird laughed.

'Of course not! Otherwise Partridge here wouldn't allow it. We went with the old fellow the first time he tried it but the crab just squatted – wouldn't go more than a few inches into the shade of the hole.'

'Then if they don't go down the hole, why does he keep trying?' she asked.

'Oh, well – I suppose he hopes to find a crab one day that will go down the burrow, but meantime he does no harm – certainly not to Partridge's precious rabbits!'

The woman was thoughtful for a moment, then she asked,

'If a crab was to go down the hole and scare out the rabbits, how would he catch them?'

'He pegs a stocking over the bolthole.'

'But you couldn't get a rabbit in a stocking!'

The laird laughed.

'You'd probably get two or three in a stocking if they saw a crab coming at 'em with a candle on its back!'

The woman reflected for some moments; then, whimsically, she asked,

'What does he do with the little crabs when he finds they won't go down the burrow?'

The laird's kindly face softened.

'He takes them back to the shore and liberates them. Humanitarian – that's what I like about the old fellow.' He shot a hard look at the keeper.

'Pity Partridge won't let him set a snare for a rabbit, but there it is – I never interfere with my keeper's decision on these matters of preserving game, but I simply could not bring myself to refuse the old chap trying with his crabs.'

The party walked in silence for some minutes. Then the laird spoke quietly, almost to himself.

'I'm told Ebbtide was a first-class, prudent seaman in his day. An able lifeboatman, dependable in an emergency and as quick-witted as they come.' He added sadly, looking directly at the gamekeeper and emphasising the words,

'It's a pity the old man has lost his wits!'

The party turned into the driveway of the laird's house.

An hour later, Ebbtide shuffled down past his cottage to the sea's edge. He lowered his tin can into the water and gently emptied out the four little green crabs and watched them scuttle away over the sandy bottom. He returned to his cottage door, looked right and left, lifted the great iron latch and entered the untidy room. He stopped at the rough wooden table beneath the small window. From some large pocket inside his capacious overcoat he pulled two fat, freshly-killed rabbits and laid them on the table. He stood looking at them for some moments, then his wrinkled brown face slowly spread into a smile. Suddenly he pulled a wry face.

'Show us the rest of your hocus-pocus!' He mimicked the keeper.

Then with surprising agility he flung off his large overcoat and unbuttoned the neck of his grubby shirt, held it open and peered down inside.

'Heigh – ho,' he crooned affectionately towards his stomach. He continued to look down while his face spread into a broad smile.

'Clever little Neptune – swift little Neptune – stewed rabbit for Ebbtide, and nice juicy livers for you!'

He reached down into his shirt and brought out a well-trained, lively, sleek brown ferret.

THE BLOCKED CHIMNEY

I WAS SENT UP HERE TO SCAPA FLOW for a spell in '42. Y'see, I'd had two continuous years in the Atlantic and Mediterranean, and I suppose I was getting noticeably irritable and callous; you can have too much of that kind of thing. And it was decided to let me off the hook and send me up here as coxswain to a Fleet auxiliary.

And that was just about the worst thing they could have done. I'd gone from the disciplined Navy to a land-locked auxiliary Navy that was happily passing away the war, manned by RNR, RNVR, Fleet Reservists and a couple of pensioners thrown in.

The captain was an RNR Lieutenant and I was truly the square peg. Fell out with everyone in the first three hours – on principle, I suppose! I upset the captain on the very next day after I'd joined the ship. It was over a stupid thing, really. Y'see, he was taking us round the ship and telling me what alterations he wanted when eventually the ship went for a short refit in Aberdeen.

Now there was a chart-locker on the bridge, and he said he wanted it taken away. Taken away? I said. Yes, he said. And I said, whatever for? He said, it's in the way. And I said, it's in the way of what? And he said, it's just in the way – and anyhow it doesn't serve any useful purpose.

And when he said that, I just about boiled over. I looked at him for a couple of seconds.

'Well, ' I said, 'you've got two little nipples on your chest; they don't serve any useful purpose either, but you don't go and get them snipped off!' My goodness, that really upset him, but the big fall-out came just about two days later.

Y'see, we had a ship's cook; he wasn't a proper Navy cook, just an RNVR seaman laddie who cooked the meat and peeled the spuds, nothing fantastic, no Fanny Craddock stuff, just plain cooking. Well, he came to me early one morning when I was doing some paperwork –

'Chief,' he said, 'the galley fire's gone out.'

I said, 'What's the matter with it?'

'The fluepipe's blocked with soot,' he said. So I said, 'Well, go and sweep it, laddie, go and sweep it! '

'Um, I can't,' he said. 'You come and see, Chief.'

So I threw down the pen and went with him to the galley and there was this range, a huge great thing, must have been made for the *Repulse* or the *Renown.* It had an eight-inch cast steel fluepipe that went up to the deckhead, and to avoid a large winch on the deck the pipe went out at an angle, right up to the corner and then up and out. Two dogleg bends and no means of sweeping it, you see. (Well, these ships were only built to be sunk, anyway!)

Well, I was puzzling how to get this thing swept when the little captain poked his head into the galley door, wanting to know where his breakfast had gone to. He was still in his pyjamas and dressing-gown, so I just let the cook do the explaining (for the captain and I were just about at the stage of writing notes to each other after the chart-locker affair).

The captain followed me up to the bridge a couple of seconds later and said,

'We'll have to take this ship over to the dockyard to get this fluepipe sorted. Go and make arrangements right away.'

So I said, 'Yeh, you do that.' I suppose I could have been forgiven, for I'd just left the Navy, where it did every job for itself; there was no excuse for not doing a job simply because you didn't have the tools; you did the job with the tools available and that could mean using anything, y'see. And here was a Navy ship going into the dockyard to get a fluepipe swept (no wonder the Germans wanted to fight us!)

Anyway, I decided to do the job the Navy way, so I grabbed a Very pistol and slipped a cartridge in it and nipped back down to the galley.

Now there were two men on deck above the galley, leaning on the guard-rail, smoking – I suppose they'd come along to eavesdrop on the captain and the cook. Anyway, I wanted this part of the deck above the galley clear, so I said:

'Hey, you men! Haven't you got any work to do? Get forrard!'

Well, they hesitated a moment, 'cause I suppose they'd never been spoken to like that before, so I repeated it –

'Go on, get forward! Move!'

They started to move and I went back into the galley, but when they saw me disappear they changed their minds and decided to finish their smoke.

Now this young cook, when he saw me barge into the galley with a gun in my hand, he almost fainted; I think he thought I was going to shoot him! Anyway, I told him to shift the big hotplate, which he did in double-quick time, and then I told him to get out of the galley. And then I stuck the brass Very pistol up the fluepipe and I pulled the trigger.

There was one heck of a thump and I nipped outside to see what had happened, and there was an atomic mushroom cloud of thick black soot over the galley – and out of its centre a green Very light sailing happily skyward. And as for those two ratings

– aah – they hadn't moved fast enough. They looked as if they'd just stepped out of the Kentucky Minstrel Show!

And the fluepipe? Y'know, the inside of that chimney was immaculate! You could even see the grey metal galvanising that was on it when it left the foundry.

OATS

I CAME TO ORKNEY in 1945 from the Navy, hoping to get work as a diver or rigger, but Metal Industries were getting ready to leave. Still, they gave me a job as a labourer, on a pick and shovel, and it supplemented my long-service Navy pension of £1 12s 6d a week, so I was quite happy.

Nearly all the labourers at Metals were crofters besides, so I decided I would be a crofter too. You see, I'd bought four acres of ground on which my cottage stood, so I thought I'd get some advice on crofting. I was pretty green on any form of horticulture – very green indeed. In the Navy I thought a potato was a potato, and that was that; I didn't know there were varieties of potato like Sharp's Express or Golden Wonder. Anyway I wanted to become a crofter, so I went along to a local farmer and told him I wanted to go into the farming business as a sideline. Come to think of it now, he must have been tickled pink. He said:

'I see you've bought some hens, so why not grow some oats for 'em?'

I thought that was a cracking idea. He said he would come and plough a bit of my ground; and he *did,* and worked it up and even sowed a half acre of oats. You know – I was fair chuffed to think I was going to own growing oats. I went out after they'd been sowed a couple of days to see if they'd started sprouting. Every morning before belting off to Metals on a motorbike, I'd go out and have a look, and one morning – a long time after their sowing – I saw a green sheen on the ground!

I could hardly get home from Metals fast enough. If I'd known about talking to plants then – I would have had a yarn with those oats night and morning. Well, in due course they ripened, so I went along to the farmer and asked him when I should have the harvest home. He said we should give them another week.

The very next morning I had my routine look at the oats, and there were scores of sparrows perched on them and pecking out the seeds. I nearly made myself ill thinking of them, down at Metals, and could hardly get home fast enough to shoo the sparrows away.

I went along to the farmer and told him the sparrows were nicking all the oats, and he said I'd have to leave the birds a share – there'd be plenty left for me. I thought, it's all right for *him* with thirty or forty acres of oats – I've only half an acre; so I thought I'd rig a scarecrow in the middle.

The sparrows fell in love with him right away. They'd perched all over him before I'd moved a dozen feet – he offered a good vantage point for them to sit on and see where the fattest oats were, so I took him down at once.

I was right worried about the sparrows (you could see where they had been doing their purloining), so I went along to one of the Melsetter gardeners, who I knew had a shotgun, and I borrowed it with two snipedust cartridges. This gun was an old one, and at some time had burst its barrels and had been sawn off, which made it ideal for what I wanted, because it would give a wide angle of fire.

So this morning, a lovely autumn day, I crept along the road to the middle of the oats, and slowly rose with the pointing gun. There seemed to be every sparrow in Melsetter on those oats. I thought, 'What a killing I'm going to have.' I bet if you could have seen my face then, you would have seen me with a satanic grin and a little pair of horns sprouting out of my forehead!

Anyway, I pulled the trigger, shifted a little, and pulled again – both barrels; and now, I thought, 'To sweep up the dead.'

I thought, before I take a sack with me to carry off the dead, I'd better go down and see the rough score, in case I need two sacks. It was funny, you know, when I fired those two barrels a whole cloud of sparrows rose and flew off. I went down among those oats and couldn't find a single dead sparrow – I hadn't killed one – not a single sparrow! I thought, those Melsetter sparrows must be armourplated.

No, I didn't kill a single bird – but I'll tell you what I *did* do: I found I'd shot the tops off of half my oats!

THE SECOND-HAND HOLE

IT ALL STARTED with young Olly Johnston getting the fright of his life. Performing his weekly chore of drawing the housebound old man's pension, he'd found the ancient 'Shoogly Tam' dead in his chair. The island doctor said he'd been dead a week, and the neighbouring fisherfolk thought this opinion was pretty near the mark, since the old man was still clutching the pension the boy had handed him the week before. He'd died of senile decay – so the doctor had also said, and the neighbours thought *that* was a pretty good diagnosis too, for old Shoogly was ninety-five.

But being both relationless and penniless, it fell the lot of the 'County' to bury him, and although his grave would be a pauper's one, it would nonetheless be rather distinctive, since he would be the first to be interred in the new cemetery.

However, the old man's demise is of small moment in this story, for it really concerns Ebbtide the beachcomber, gravedigger for the North Parish of the island, and Willie the Prune who performed the similar macabre work for the South Parish, each man averaging a steady four holes a year at twelve shillings a hole.

But little graveyards, like mighty empires, have their day; and Ebbtide the beachcomber had come to the point where, so to speak, he'd dug himself out of a job.

His half-acre of burial ground had swallowed its last guest; it was full – gorged – satisfied, its inmates pinned securely beneath a hundred tons of slabs, open books, obelisks, cherubs and weeping angels. Now its rusting Edwardian wrought iron gates could be finally shut and locked; the ivy, dockans, mosses and lichens could take over; and the whole could rest in peace.

The new quarter-acre of burial ground – a rough square of heather peatland by the shore – was duly consecrated by the plump old minister in the presence of the laird and McBray the district councillor. It lay on the other side of the narrow burn that ran beside the wall of the old kirkyard.

Now this little burn turned out to be the villain of the piece, for it marked the boundary between the North and South parishes, so while St Just's kirk and its old graveyard stood in the North Parish, its new cemetery now stood in the South Parish, and nobody on the little island would have dreamed of taking advantage of this curious situation except the shrivelled little Willie the Prune.

Returning from the consecrating ceremony astride Titus, the thirty-year-old ex-farm Clydesdale, the minister was met at the manse door by the little South Parish gravedigger, who broke the fresh news:

'Shoogly's deid!'

The minister leaned forward in the saddle.

'I beg your pardon?'

'Shoogly Tam – he's awa – deid!'

The minister slowly regained an upright position and fixed a thoughtful gaze between Titus's limp ears. The Prune added quickly:

' – an' *I* digs his grave!' His face spread into a grin.

'You're – you're not serious, Willie – that's Ebbtide's province!' The satanic grin on the Prune's face widened.

'Not *it* – that new boneyard's on the South Parish, an' I'm the South Parish gravedigger!'

Incredulous, the minister looked down into the upturned face, permitting himself the unkind thought that 'The Prune' was an excellent name. All the same, the fellow had a point. Nobody had thought of this snag arising, and he was not in a position to make a decision himself. It was serious – he would see the laird! He dismounted and dismissed Titus with a gentle slap on the rump. Turning, he said,

'Don't do anything until I tell you, Willie – tomorrow – perhaps.' The Prune, grinning, backed away, then turned and shuffled off through the gate.

It was later that evening that Titus clopped slowly up the drive of the laird's house with the thoughtful old minister, who was now wondering if the laird was the right person to go to first. Perhaps he should have gone to Councillor McBray instead; after all, it was the local district council that nominated the gravediggers.

But then, McBray was a distant cousin of the Prune, and he was also such a cagey fellow – he would beat about the bush, never committing himself, cleverly avoiding the question, then end loudly about calling a meeting; and that would take days – and poor old Shoogly!

The minister was suddenly aware that Titus had stopped by the stone veranda, and the laird, puffing a pipe, was watching him through the open French window. Knowing the laird was kindly disposed towards Ebbtide, he prepared himself for the explosion to come and, without dismounting, recounted his meeting with the Prune. The laird listened, controlling himself with evident effort, until he could do so no more.

'The little pipsqueak – muscling in, eh? Send him to me, b'George – I'll put a flea in his ear!'

But the minister would have none of *that* – and said so. He wagged his head and pointed out that the district council should have taken the gravedigger into consideration when they allocated the new ground; should have taken nothing 'for granted' – they should have laid down the rules, properly; no, McBray was the man – he was the chairman, and he must make the decision. The minister would go and see him first thing in the morning! He turned the still-munching horse, and thumped the heels of his gumboots into the sagging belly. The laird watched the retreating pair.

'You're wasting your time, Padre!' Then, a final thought coming to mind, the laird shouted:

'Get that goat McBray up here – seven tomorrow evening!'

Next morning, as he rode away from McBray's house, the minister admitted to himself that the laird was right. He had wasted his time. He could not pin the fellow down to a straight answer, although he had promised to discuss the matter at the laird's house.

And so it was that shortly after seven that evening, the serious old minister and the complacent McBray presented themselves in the laird's drawing-room. The laird was blunt.

'You know the position, McBray, and who's the gravedigger for the new ground!'

'We'll decide that at our next meeting!'

' – And when's *that?*'

'In – ah – two months' time!' He smiled. The laird reddened, then,

' – And what about old Shoogly Tam in the meantime – hey?'

The councillor spread his hands.

'Ohhh – old Tam! Now there's no need to worry about him – we'll get the county roadmen to dig *his* grave!'

The minister objected at once. No, no, that would be quite wrong. Ebbtide and Willie had dug the graves for thirty and twenty-five years respectively. No, it must be one or the other – no third party – and McBray must make the decision!

But McBray intended to do nothing of the kind. He was rather enjoying the situation. He'd offered a solution, and the laird could take it or leave it. The big laird's face grew redder, his chin jutted. He looked at the two men: the minister, carefully considering his statements lest he be unjust to anybody, and the other, plausible, glib, easily extricating himself when driven to a corner. There came an awkward moment of silence. McBray, sure of himself, hooked his thumbs into his waistcoat, rocked gently on heels and toes, cocked his head to one side, affected a smile and said,

'O'course, I could invoke the wisdom o' Solomon an' say they could dig half the grave each. Hee – heee!'

The laird rose to the remark like a salmon to the fly.

'Right!' he almost roared. *'That's* the solution! Well done, McBray – I second that proposal – I take it you agree, Padre? That's settled, then – I'll inform the parties – I'll act as umpire – ten o' clock in the morning – half the grave each – splendid, splendid – !'

The minister stood, open-mouthed, unbelieving. McBray began to protest, but the laird, talking loudly, ushered both men through the door and slammed it shut.

Next morning, ten minutes before the appointed time, McBray arrived at the ground. He had not intended to be at the funeral, but he was worried. He would be made to look a fool! He would get the laird to call off this ridiculous thing. He would call an emergency meeting of the council that very evening and get the thing settled – the laird couldn't take a joke! By Jove, he'd give the laird a piece of his mind when he arrived. For the next ten minutes he paced the ground, choosing his words, formulating his phrases, working himself up.

The Prune arrived on his squeaking bicycle, his pick and shovel lashed to the crossbar. He grinned at McBray, his distant relative. Then Ebbtide on foot, followed by the sleepy Titus with the minister, and lastly the kilted laird in his car. The laird lost no time. He began at once to address the little party, organising the affair, laying down the rules – the colonel again, addressing his troops. Ebbtide and Willie would dig foot and foot about – three feet each for six shillings apiece. He produced a coin from the pouch on his sporran and held it ready to flick. Looking down at the Prune, he asked,

'Heads or tails?'

'Heids!'

It came down tails.

'Right! – Ebbtide digs the first foot!'

The willing Ebbtide applied himself to the job. McBray looked on sullenly, his fire having disappeared with the arrival of the laird. Ebbtide finished his generous first foot and climbed out. The Prune, ready to jump down, peered into the beachcomber's face.

'I wish it wis *your* grave I wis diggin!'

A sharp rebuke from the laird sent him quickly about his task. And so the grave went down; foot – by – foot. Ebbtide finished his third and last dig and came up.

'Right!' boomed the laird. 'Ebbtide – go and get Shoogly Tam while Willie finishes the hole!'

Titus, the island's funeral horse, now fully awake and cropping at the grass verge, suddenly found himself following Ebbtide at the end of a short rope tether, and in his horsey wisdom knew the business in hand; for whenever he followed Ebbtide he knew he would be harnessed to the bright-blue painted, two-wheeled farm cart that always stood above the beachcomber's cottage. But he did not mind; the load was always light, always a long box, with sometimes rings of scentless flowers growing out of its top.

Willie the Prune had just finished the hole as the jolting blue cart came into view around the bend in the road, the august Titus taking his time – as if sensing the occasion – his great hooves clacking on the stony road in near funeral march time. He halted of his own accord abreast the little group some thirty yards distant. For a moment nobody moved except the old minister,who produced his little book. Then Ebbtide stood up in the cart, cupped his hands and shouted:

' – He's awa!'

The laird's eyes narrowed. He bellowed back:

'Whadder – ya – mean, he's awa?'

' – Old Shoogly Tam. His neebors didna think he'd keep ower muckle langer, so they buried him this morn roond at the sooth side boneyard!'

* * * * * * * * * *

For twenty years the hole remained; and open books, obelisks, cherubs and slabs sprang up around it, for even the kindly, tolerant island people draw the line at accepting a second-hand hole; and it might have been forgotten from that day to this, had not the tinker woman 'Kate the bogle', weeping loudly into a large green handkerchief that prevented her from seeing where she was going, fallen into it, and smartly clambered out again, roundly cursing everybody, and lairds and councillors in particular.

But this story can now be told because the hole has gone. It has now an occupant; and the kindly Ebbtide, knowing the grave is never likely to boast a headstone, has made a rough white-painted wooden cross upon which is painted in black letters in an amateurish hand:

Here Lies
Wilberforce John Emmanuel McBray

And should you be a casual visitor to the little island cemetery, and ask Ebbtide the beachcomber who it was that rejoiced in this impressive name, he will tell you that it once belonged to a gentleman who was better known as 'Willie the Prune'.

PHIT! – NAE FUSH?

AS CUSTOMS OFFICER, I made every endeavour to keep to the precise times in my programme of patrols, but today the puncture in the pelting rain had left me wet, muddy, irritable, and half an hour behind. And now the trawler, nosing her way into the Golden Wharf at Lyness, would further keep me out in the downpour.

Her skipper, a middle-aged little man with kindly blue eyes, triple-jerseyed and with a week's growth, leaned on the opened wheelhouse window-frame, his jaws champing slowly on some seemingly indestructible delicacy.

He was watching two of his deckhands aft, who were having trouble with a large wooden oiling fender that prevented the trawler's stern from coming alongside. For some three minutes he watched them, all the while champing his jaws and spitting out of the window at almost exact intervals; then, leaning out, he shouted an order to the two men in broad Aberdonian, of which I did not understand a single word.

The bow of the trawler was now alongside, and the skipper and I were some twenty feet apart. He turned his face towards me, fixing me with a look of melancholy interest. Impatiently, curtly, I asked the formal question: 'Are you carrying stores, skipper?'

He pushed his chew into one cheek, then, 'Phit?'

' Are you carrying spirits and tob— ?'

'Ohhh! – aye, aye!' he cut in quickly.

I would have to go on board and place his duty-free stores under seal. The rain was now drumming and I was thoroughly soaked. The two men aft had cleared the wooden fender and were now hauling the stern flat alongside. I looked down onto the streaming trawler's deck, cluttered with sea wrack, chats, guttings and jellyfish. I would jump down the five feet or so from the wharf to the deck and so sat down, regardless of the puddle, on the granite coping of the wharf, and was preparing to jump when the skipper suddenly leaned right out of his window and shouted for'ard, 'Hamish, get the Customs a fry!'

'I don't want any fish,' I told him, my legs dangling over the wharf.

'Phit?'

'I – don't – want – any – fish!' I spaced the words.

'Ye dinna want ony fush – ?'

'No.'

'Phit?'

'NO!' I barked.

He recommenced his chewing, regarding me thoughtfully for some moments, then –

'D'ye no like fush?' he asked incredulously.

'Yes.'

'Phit?'

'YESs' I spoke loudly.

'Ye do like fush, eh – Hamish, get the Customs a fry.' He shouted again.

'But I don't *WANT* any fish!' This time I shouted.

'Phit?'

'OH, GO TO THE DEVIL!'

I jumped down onto the wet cluttered deck, putting my foot onto a jellyfish and slipped flat on my back among the guttings.

I still like fish – but not jellyfish.

Strangely enough, tragedy often lurks at the heart of a favourite story. This next animal tale shows how Harry brings his practical, down-to-earth sense of humour to bear on a situation which other people would have treated differently; that is, if they had the temerity to befriend a toad in the first place ...

NAPOLEON

OH YEH, the toad; I called him Napoleon. Y'see, it was dusk one evening when I went out to shut the garage doors. Now, it'd been raining and in the middle of the road was a puddle, and in the middle of the puddle was a stone – y'know, a flat stone – and sitting on this stone was a toad – a half-grown toad. So I bent down and spoke to him an' tickled his head, y'know; and he didn't seem to mind and he looked so lonely on his little island, so I called him Napoleon.

Now my wife is fond of all living creatures, so I picked him up and I took him indoors, and I told my wife to close her eyes an' open her hands (y'know the sort of thing) and I dropped him in. She held him up and looked at him and tickled his head and spoke to him (y'know, the way women do), and we put him outside the door, hoping that he would take up residence in the garden.

Now where we'd put him, it turned out to be a proper toady Shangri La, y'see, because it was right under a lighted window and the heather moths flying at the light were knocking themselves senseless on the glass (or some of them were) and dropping to the ground. Napoleon had never had it so good. Well, he came back nearly every night for the next coupla months.

Now, he didn't actually live in the garden; he used to go under the gate and hop across the road to a wet patch on the other side, y'see. Most nights, always at darkening (that's lamp-lighting time), he'd hop across the road and take up situation under the window. He grew into a real toady heavyweight. In fact, he was the only toad I've ever seen with a double chin – he was a right whopper!

Well, one day I'd been down to an oil-ship at Lyness, and I came home in the car and I turned the corner in the road and I drove straight up into the garage. And then I suddenly remembered it was lamp-lighting time and I thought 'Oh, golly – Napoleon!' So I whipped down the road quick and oh! there was Napoleon; I'd flattened him with the front tyre and I really ironed him out with the Town and Country tyre on the back. He was flat as ... well, as half a sheet of toilet paper. I was going to say, you could just about have posted him through a crack in a plaster ceiling.

Anyway, I picked him up by two corners and I took him indoors and I held him up and I said, 'Look! – Napoleon!' My wife almost burst into tears and I thought it was a tactless thing for me to say, so I said: 'Well, I'll give him a Christian burial.'

Now, at the bottom of our garden, we've got a grotto, where we've buried all our pets over the years, so I took Napoleon down there and I knelt down and I laid him out flat on the grass. Y'know, I looked at him and somehow I felt very sad – I even hoped that he'd gone to some toady Valhalla where he'd be surrounded by lighted windows and a never-ending hatch of heather moths knocking themselves against the glass – y'know, sort of eternal manna.

Well, I realised that I was getting a bit sentimental, so I took out my pocket-knife and dug a little hole, and I picked up Napoleon and I folded him neatly in four and dropped him in.

THE PHILOSOPHER

HE WAS a lawyer, philosopher, and a Communist. He was also the ship's cook. This I had learnt in the ten-minute rummage of his little galley. His teenage disciple sat on the coal bunker, munching steadily on a large ball of pink bubblegum. Above his neck-length shock of black hair sat a miniature stetson, as one may come by at a fairground, its yellow fringe scintillating in time with the champing of his unshaven jaws. A half-circle of green card stuck on its front announced 'Deadwood Stage'.

For ten minutes I had been forced to listen to the philosopher at the stove, ceaselessly prodding the contents of a half-dozen babbling pots with a large iron skewer, the while delivering himself of a catalogue of grievances, Communist clichés and remembered phrases. His strident reiteration irritated me beyond endurance – I felt I must stop him. Quickly I turned and faced him.

'Yours?' I held up the pocket-sized transistor at face level.

He nodded.

'Receipt?'

No, he'd no receipt, but I was satisfied with his excuse. I was not interested in the bauble anyway, but I had stopped him – dead; he'd lost the place in his party piece, this Lenin, drawn to his full height before his pots, addressing an imaginary legion – and I had tapped him gently behind the knees. I re-hung the set on a large wire nail above some unpeeled potatoes. At once it began to squawk the news:

' – Cape Canaveral – American space probe with dogs on board – '

Insolently, he pushed past me and snapped it off.

'Bliddy cruel!'

'Eh?'

'Bliddy cruel!' He emphasised the words.

'Oh!'

He looked at me for some seconds; then, lowering his voice for full effect,

'Don't you think it's cruel – firing dumb creatures up there!' He thumbed towards the deckhead. I did not answer. Affecting to be overcome by the inhumanity of the whole affair, he almost exploded:

'No, no! – by hokey, no! You don't care – !'

For fully a minute he launched into a torrent of invective, clamorous, exciting himself with his own noise. He stopped suddenly.

'How would you like to be fired up there against your will?' he asked truculently.

'I wouldn't,' I answered truthfully.

'Well then!' This was the final, devastating statement. He swung round on his pots and recommenced his prodding in silence.

I felt a little sorry for him. I abominated his Communism, but warmed to him as a humanitarian, a lover of animals, a protector of creatures; and reflecting that 'it takes all sorts', I was about to leave when he pushed past me, and from under a sack in the corner he lifted a large live lobster that I had noticed during the rummage. Wrenching a lid from a large boiling pot, he swung the creature over it, waited until its tail stopped clapping and its great claws hung passively down, then he opened his finger and thumb and let it drop down into the scalding water.

We watched it struggle and convulse for some seconds as the searing heat penetrated its shell. Then it lay very still. We watched it turn from deep metallic blue, through shades of purple to scarlet.

Slowly he replaced the lid. Thoughtfully, quietly, he said, 'Them Yanks ain't got no feeling for dumb creatures.'

TITUS OUTSIDER

I DON'T see old McTaggart about much these days, and perhaps that is not surprising – he is almost ninety. I did meet up with him at the island's annual ploughing match recently; he was glaring at the dozen gaudily-painted tractors lined up for the start.

'Monsters of metal and rubber, their great power-packed iron bellies gorged with oil, reeking of exhaust and hot grease, smugly sitting back on their huge driving wheels; their twin shares poised, ready to stab the sleeping earth and tear it apart to an accompaniment of rumble and clatter … And fifty years ago: a dozen 'pair o' horse', quiet, patiently waiting, paper roses adorning their manes and tails, the only sounds the subdued thud of the hooves, the chink of a chain, the deep breathing from the great chests of the straining brutes; and the odours, the faint ammoniacal smell of the horses and the sweet, pungent newly-turned earth.'

Of course, old McTaggart didn't say that. He didn't use such words or phrasing – but I knew that was what he was thinking. He turned to me, shifted his chew of black twist and said,

'Did I ever tell ye about Ebbtide and Titus at the trotting race?'

I dived for my shorthand pad, for the old man has a wealth of stories about his one-time crewmate of the sail and oar-driven lifeboat *Annie Miles*; sharing the same thwart, sweating her along by oars through many a storm. But the story he told me was this time not about the sea.

If anyone has ever come close to concocting the elixir of life, then it must have been the island crofter 'Willie the Prune', as all would have testified who had sampled the potent Witches' Brew of treacle brandy that dribbled from his illicit still. Old Ebbtide the beachcomber, who sometimes drove the thirty-year-old Clydesdale Titus, would readily agree, for although he only tasted the stuff once, he has absolute faith in its remarkable properties.

But this story begins in the little meeting-room of the island's village hall where Councillor McBray, chairman of the local crofters' society, has been suggesting some innovations for the forthcoming agricultural show; and it has been decided to ask the newly-formed Sea Scouts drum and bugle band to give a parade or two on the showground and – something really new – a Clydesdale trotting race! The laird is to make the rules, and act as umpire, and Councillor McBray has promised to make a book on the race – giving half the winnings to the crofters' society treasurer.

'But supposing you get rooked?' somebody asked. McBray beamed, then with affected solemnity:

'In that case, gentlemen, I'll pay the loss out of my own pocket.'

But everyone present knew the rapacious McBray was the last person in the room who would allow himself to be rooked. Somebody brightened things up further by asking:

'Supposing Ebbtide turns up with Titus – what handicap for them?'

Everybody laughed; McBray answered jauntily,

'Since you're talking of the funeral cart, we'll get 'em to give a funeral march!' He chuckled at his own remark.

It was old McTaggart himself that gave Ebbtide the news of the previous evening's meeting, and was rather surprised to see a faint smile come onto the beachcomber's face. He thought that McBray's reference to Titus, the ancient ex-farm Clydesdale that Ebbtide occasionally borrowed from the minister, would have made him angry; instead, the beachcomber said thoughtfully,

'You say the Sea Scouts drum and bugle band will be there!' The other nodded. Ebbtide smiled more broadly, winked heavily, nodded sideways towards his cottage, and the two men went inside.

The news of the forthcoming trotting race did not, at first, arouse much interest among the islanders; but as the days went by it became generally known that four crofters had entered their Clydesdales for the race, and were indeed in surreptitious training. There was Jemima, the seven-year-old mare, being put through her paces down on the west shore of the island; Duncan the big chestnut, doing a nightly two-mile stretch on the south side; the powerful Gideon, the one-tonner, going like a traction engine on the north side every evening; and the big mare Jeannie of Toddyhouse. Within a week the coming event was the topic of the day, and when it became known that Ebbtide had entered the ancient Titus for the race, excitement reached fever pitch.

For the next fortnight the four farm-working Clydesdales that had been entered were in strict training. The laird had made the rules, and the one that concerned the competitors most was:

'If a horse breaks into a gallop, it must be stopped at once, and backed, so that the cart wheels turn in the opposite direction.'

Now, stopping a one-ton Clydesdale in a gallop is difficult enough, but to make him step backwards by simply hauling back on the reins is something of a feat, since walking backwards is not in the curriculum of plough-horse training. And after a great many futile attempts at this, the drivers found it much quicker to haul the galloping beast to a halt, jump down from the cart, grasp the bridle and growl a few well-chosen remarks together with a hefty shove on the horse's muzzle; after which the beast would clumsily oblige. But this procedure sometimes took valuable minutes, and must therefore be avoided; and each driver came to the same conclusion – that the safest way was to get the horse into a trot, then let it go at its own speed, remembering that it was fatal to encourage the beast by shouting or rein flicking, which would be likely to send it into a canter.

Titus spent his days as usual, browsing in the minister's field untroubled by any kind of 'training'. Indeed, the last time he had even been between a pair of shafts had been three months before when, as the island's funeral horse, he had hauled old Tam o' Haybrake to the cemetery; but now he had a similar chore, for another old worthy had died, Archie McCantick, and there was some speculation about Ebbtide combining business with training and trotting old McCantick to the graveyard – to the consternation of the half-dozen mourners who would be following the cart on foot. But as before, Titus performed his task at funeral march speed.

After the funeral, however, Ebbtide stopped Titus at the kirkyard gate. Then, leaning over the frontboard of the cart, he gave the horse a hefty smack on the rump; and Titus, who was prone to fall immediately into a state of semi-sleep whenever he was stopped, was so surprised at this treatment that he set off at once in a shambling trot, which quickly decreased into his usual walk. But Ebbtide was determined to have him trotting; and, snatching off his battered homburg, he laid about the horse's rump with it. And so they trotted home, Titus completing his one and only training session for the forthcoming race.

The day of the show broke fine and calm. The flags and pennants decorating the showground hung limp; the smoke from the tin fluepipe at the back of the big canvas refreshment marquee rose straight into the air. To the casual observer it would appear an ideal day; it was also an ideal day for the flies and midges. The livestock in the pens, like the exhibitors, judges and visitors to the ground, were almost demented by bites and stings. The Sea Scouts bugle band with some fifty supporters had arrived from the main island, and were now being entertained in the big marquee with cream buns and ginger beer. The judging would be finished by three o'clock, and the field sports would start, culminating in the star event of the day, the half-mile trotting race.

The two-wheeled farm carts were already on the field, shining in bright blue paint with wheels and shafts in red, green and yellow. Only Ebbtide's cart was absent; but perhaps, some said, since it was the island's funeral cart, its presence might dampen the happy, expectant atmosphere.

The competing Clydesdales were not yet present, but at ten minutes to four they would be on the field for harnessing. Councillor McBray was having a field day with the betting, and he was delighted that his own idea had aroused so much interest – and said so, loudly.

The mare Jemima was favourite, being backed by almost everyone from the populous west side. Now she stood at two to one on; Duncan, Jeannie and Gideon were evens. There were no bets on Titus.

At ten to four promptly, the shining horses arrived, and for the next ten minutes the polished harness with glittering brasses was being adjusted. At four-thirty the horses were on the line, and the laird stood ready with the starting gun. Somebody shouted:

'Here's Ebbtide and Titus!'

Everyone turned to watch Ebbtide and the old horse come through the five-barred farm gate and go behind the big marquee. All eyes watched the other end of the tent for the reappearance of the turnout, but Ebbtide appeared on foot at the first end. The large excited crowd fell into expectant silence as he shuffled up to McBray and said,

'What odds Titus?' McBray hesitated for a moment, then:

'Twenty to one!'

A loud murmur of disapproval rose from the crowd. The laird growled:

'B'George, McBray – you're taking no chances – what?'

'Well, then – fifty to one – remember I'm giving half the winnings to the society and paying any losses out of my own pocket!'

The laird's face reddened, his chin jutted; the crowd began to remonstrate about the already mean odds offered. Somebody began to chant; it was quickly taken up by the whole crowd:

'Hundred to one – hundred to one – hundred to one – !'

McBray swung round on the crowd.

'All right – all right – hundred to one, then, but no more bets on Titus!'

Ebbtide produced a crumpled pound note and handed it to McBray. The laird, already impatient at the delay, roared,

'Right – now come on, Ebbtide, you're holding up the whole thing.'

Ebbtide shuffled back behind the marquee. Diving into the capacious pocket of his overcoat, he brought out a bottle of the Prune's home-brewed ale, poured it into a tin basin and offered it to Titus who drank it with relish.

The old horse brightened at once; he licked his lips, his limp ears stiffened, he stamped his hind hooves as if impatient to be off. Ebbtide jumped up into the cart, flicked the reins, and trotted up to the starting line. Almost at once the laird bellowed:

'*Stand by!*'

Then came the loud report of the gun, and simultaneously the explosive cheer of the crowd, the blowing of the bugles and beating of the drums, the ear-piercing screaming of the children.

The farm Clydesdales, used to the quiet of the fields and already tormented by the flies and midges, were shattered by the sudden unearthly racket of noise. Jemima the mare reared, almost coming back into the cart and throwing the driver back out over the tailboard; then she landed with a thud and broke straight into a gallop out across the field, driverless. Duncan reared and came down at right angles to the course, galloping round and back across the starting line, the wheel of the cart splintering as it smashed into the field dyke. Jeannie and Gideon, flanks quivering, started in a canter for a few strides, then Jeannie broke into a gallop, Gideon following her.

The drivers, arms straight out, foot against the front board, hauled back with every ounce. The big mare stopped, reared, pawed the air, then came down heavily across the path of Gideon. The two carts crashed, the wheels becoming locked, the earth reverberating beneath the thudding hooves; the drivers jumped down, seizing the bridles, cursing, vociferating. Jeannie refused to quieten, shaking her head, trying to wrench free, her eyes rolling. Gideon, after several minutes wrestling with his driver and anchored by the locked carts, stamped back a pace or two, freeing the wheel and turning it backwards. The laird, mounted on a hack and watching the wheels, roared,

'Right!'

The driver scrambled back into the cart, and gently slapped the reins; and Gideon started off in a fast trot, leaving the still-stamping, unpacified Jeannie. The laird had been so involved with the locked carts that he had momentarily forgotten about Titus, who he now saw clopping happily round the quarter-mile pole. It was now between Gideon and Titus, who had a three-hundred-yard lead, but the giant young horse was stepping really fast, his driver holding him in with a taut, delicate rein.

The crowd watched in silence as the big horse rounded the pole and began to overhaul the veteran. Now they were a hundred yards from the line; Ebbtide saw the handsome head and shining arched neck of Gideon appear abreast the wheel of his cart. Snatching off his homburg, he laid about the rump of Titus; the old horse responded for a few strides, but Ebbtide could see that he was done. Titus had given his best; his head was down, his ears limp – he began to stumble. His last rally had only taken Ebbtide to the edge of the crowd, which had fallen into a sympathetic silence for the veteran's gallant effort.

The beachcomber watched the massive froth-flecked shoulders of Gideon go past, with jingling brasses, the creak of straining leather, the rhythmic thudding of hooves – twenty-five yards to go. Titus, now completely spent, had dropped to a trembling walk. McBray, on the finishing line, was beaming. And then it happened: like a detonated mine the crowd exploded. The children shrieked, the bugles blasted, the drums boomed and rattled – and Gideon, terrified at the sudden shattering of the silence, bolted, crossing the line at a disqualifying gallop.

His face flushed with anger, but trying to smile affably, McBray paid Ebbtide the total stake money plus a ten-pound cheque from his own pocket to make up the balance. The old beachcomber smiled – he knew he would win. He knew those kids would kick up that racket – for his old crewmate, McTaggart, on a promise of half the stake-money, had been among those kids as cheerleader – and he knew those quiet farm horses would go to pieces with all the noise!

Up by the marquee, the laird, watching Titus enjoy a bucket of cool spring water and talking quietly to Ebbtide, suddenly began to chuckle, then to laugh. He bent forward and howled with laughter. He went on laughing – Ebbtide had told him why he'd entered the race – old Titus was stone deaf!

BOATSHED FANTASY

THE LIFEBOAT ENGINEER had watched the quill brush I was using for almost fifteen minutes, as I inscribed the recent service that would make the final entry on the record board.

'One more completed board, and both the boatshed walls will be full,' he said. I looked round the shed, its varnished walls and roof reflecting back the polished brasses and royal blue of the lifeboat's hull. The old record boards were screwed permanently into place, some faded, going back almost a hundred years, telling of dramatic rescues of sailing ship crews, reminiscent of storm-force wind and turbulent, confused seas, of drumming canvas and droning, vibrant cordage, of sail-driven lifeboats with straining oarsmen, of crude and primitive effort – and now the new boat, the *TGB*, powerful, sleek, confident, ready to launch in a matter of minutes.

'Maybe she won't be here long enough to fill another board,' I said.

'How come that?' the engineer grinned.

'Perhaps she'll be replaced by a helicopter!'

His grin broadened – a little patronisingly, I thought. He laid the keys of the boatshed on the table beside me.

'I'm going for dinner. Drop the keys in at my cottage as you pass.'

He left me alone in the cathedral-like silence of the shed, a little annoyed by his parting grin. I was about to hang the completed blackboard in its place when, in a soft, deep, even voice, I heard:

'Do you really *think a helicopter could replace me?'*

I lowered the board, swung round and faced the boat.

'Did *you* say that?' I asked her.

'Yes.'

Somehow I was not surprised. In a whimsical kind of way, or by some sublimate faculty of mind, I have always regarded ships and boats as *living* things.

'Well, I don't see why not,' I replied.

'You're not serious!'

'I certainly am. Helicopters have proved themselves very efficient in rescue work.'

'Have *they?'*

There was something in the way she passed this last remark that annoyed me as much as the engineer's grin.

'Well,' I said, 'if only for sentiment's sake we'll all be sorry to see you and your kind go, but we must advance with the times – you've had your day and must surrender to more efficient methods.'

'More efficient?'

'Yes, more *efficient* – the helicopter is more efficient than you, just as you are more efficient than *your* predecessors.'

' – *But I'm* not *more efficient than my predecessors!* '

'Of course you are! – You can't be equated with the old *Annie Miles* with her sails and oars.'

'Look,' said the lifeboat, *'I think you're using the word "efficient" in the wrong context. My elder sister* Annie Miles *did everything she was asked to do – she may have taken a good deal more time to do it, but she* did *it* – efficiently.'

I began to lose my temper. I'd always thought of craft like lifeboats and 'J' class yachts as thoroughbreds – and sometimes thoroughbreds can be a little temperamental, but the *TGB* here was plainly out for an argument. There was a full minute's silence, then she asked,

'What do you mean by efficient?'

'Efficient, – well, – efficient means – capable.' I grabbed the word out of the air.

'Well then, my elder sister was as capable of rescuing a shipwrecked crew as I am.'

'But, good heavens, you're faster – and better found!'

'Oh, you mean I'm more manageable and comfortable!'

'Exactly!'

'Well, you know, when we lifeboats are launched, the object of the exercise is to pick up shipwrecked men – and they *don't care tuppence whether they are being hauled into my old sister or me.'*

I was beginning to boil. She was just trying to be downright awkward. She knew perfectly well what I meant. Anyway, I wasn't going to walk out on the argument. My eye caught the brand-new tumbler lock that had just been fitted to the workshop door. I would drive my point home with that.

'See that lock?' I spoke slowly. 'It's a new and more efficient lock than the old mortice lock.'

'Is it?'

'Yes; it's a modern, brass, tumbler lock and has superseded the iron mortice lock which was old-fashioned – done – finished. It's more – *efficient.*' I spaced the last words.

'I shouldn't have thought it.'

'Why?'

'The engineer locked himself out with it yesterday, and he couldn't have done that with the old lock!'

I was boiling over, stung. A long silence followed and I simmered down. Controlling my voice, I said, changing the point, 'You can say what you like, but you've got to admit that a rescue helicopter can do all that you can do – and in a fraction of the time it takes you to do it!'

'Oh!'

'Yes, a *fraction* of the time.'

'What about the Oljaren, *then – she carried a crew of forty-one!'*

I remembered the Norwegian tanker lying on the Pentland Skerries, battered, pounded, with half her bottom ground out by the rocks. The lifeboat went on, *'That would have required ten lifts by the helicopter of half an hour each – that's five hours!'*

'Well, what about it?' I said.

'My predecessor, Thomas McCunn, *did the whole thing in fifty minutes!'*

' – But that was an isolated case!'

'All right then, give me another instance – from the board you're holding.'

I scanned the board quickly but couldn't see a service that would prove my point. I felt my anger rise again. After a moment she went on, *'Very well then, let's take the* Strathcoe.'

She was goading me, of course. I remembered the *Strathcoe* was slap up against a 450-foot cliff face with an enormous overhang of rock, and only after a superb feat of seamanship was the trawler's crew taken off as the ship was grinding to pieces beneath them. There was another silence, and she seemed to know what I was thinking, for she said, *'What about the* Ben Barvas, *then?'* and added, *'She was in open water.'*

I remembered that one too. Pitch black and a screaming Force Ten with driving, suffocating spindrift. No other thing in the whole world could have saved her crew except a lifeboat. I was very angry indeed now. I picked up the record board and hung it in its place. I went over to the boatshed door, opened it, and turned. Controlling my voice, I said:

'It just happens that you have made a case for yourself with a couple of isolated rescues, but we must move with the times. The helicopter is the rescue craft of tomorrow. You're done – outmoded. You're like the horse, the steam locomotive, the battleship. You're outdated, finished – a museum piece – ! '

I went out and slammed the door.

* * * * * * * * * *

Yesterday I went over to the boatshed to give the record board its final coat of varnish. The boat bay was empty.

'Where's the lifeboat?' I asked a man greasing the slipway.

'She's awa oot,' he said without looking up.

'I can see that – where's she gone?'

He straightened up.

'Oot to the Firth to pick up the crew of a crashed helicopter.'

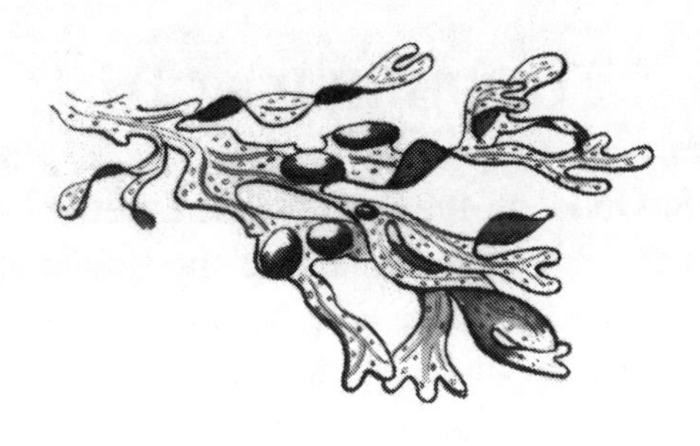

GOPHER WOOD

SHE WAS ONE of the larger seine-netters and new to Longhope. I felt I should make the acquaintance of her skipper, so I boarded her and went below.

The crew, together with some fishermen from another seine-netter lying alongside, were sitting at the table in the crew's after cabin. At the bottom of the ladder I stopped, turned, and looked around. Eight pairs of eyes were fixed on my face; nobody spoke. On the cabin table was spread a clean newspaper on which stood several large mugs, a thickly sliced loaf, a fresh cake of margarine on a tin plate, and a large steaming tea-urn. I scanned the faces quickly, then,

'Skipper?' I asked. The ship's cook spoke.

'He's no here!' He went on, 'He'll just be!' – then added further,

'Want a mug o' tea – Customs?'

I was in no hurry and, wanting to appear sociable, I accepted and sat below the ladder near a hot iron bogey stove. The engineer, a small, middle-aged greying man in a clean well-washed blue overall, sat on the locker seat opposite, contentedly puffing a pipe.

Suddenly came a commotion at the ladder top, then thigh-length seaboots came down, followed by the large stern of the skipper. He stopped at the bottom, turned, scowled round the faces as if counting, then mounted the locker-seat and trod unceremoniously between the men to the table head and eased himself down onto the locker-seat. Without looking up, he raised his arms directly above his head, grasped a huge brass-bound Bible from a shelf, and dropped it on the table with a thump. Still scanning the faces, he dug his fingers into the pages at random and threw the book open. Still without looking, he pointed a finger at a part of the page, looked down and began to read. I removed my cap.

'Make thee an ark of gopher wood; rooms shalt thou make in the ark, and shalt pitch it within and – '

The little engineer, arms folded and still enjoying his smoke, took the pipe from his mouth, looked at the skipper, then,

'Make it of *what?'* he asked with a note of incredulity.

The skipper stopped reading, fixed the engineer with a belligerent stare, then re-read the sentence to himself. Looking up, he said,

'Gopher wood! '

'Gopher wood?'

'Aye – GOPHER WOOD!'

'Never heard of it!'

'Phit?'

'Never heard of it – there ain't no such wood!' The engineer leaned back and re-started his pipe-puffing, returning his gaze to the red-hot bogey top.

'Hoh! – so there ain't no such wood, eh? – well, it says here it *was* gopher wood!' The skipper thumped the book with his knuckles.

'I don't care what it says there!' The engineer spoke quietly, without removing his pipe or shifting his gaze.

Knuckles still on the book, the skipper leaned forward with a menacing out-thrust of his lower jaw. Quivering with wrath, he shouted:

'If you don't believe in gopher wood – you're a – a – disbelieving – disbelieving – SKLITE!'

To the skipper, this appellation, created with the suddenness of a thunderclap, was the final insult; he could think of no worse name to call the engineer. He stood, visibly shaking with temper. He slammed the big book shut with such force that the mugs jumped. Inarticulate with rage, he shouted:

'Any disbelieving BLANKer what don't BLANKingwell believe in BLANKing gopher wood, don't BLANKingwell believe in BLANKall!'

Next time I'll keep my blanking cap on!

CHRISTMAS CARD STAR

ALMOST FORTY YEARS AGO he'd received his first Christmas parcel from the laird's wife, and smilingly she'd told him not to open it until Christmas Day. He'd received his parcel each year since, and although she had never repeated her first request, old David the shepherd had respected it.

At dawn this Christmas Eve he knew the snow was coming, had taken the dogs up to the moor and brought down the five hundred ewes to shelter, had collected his parcel from the laird's good lady and returned to his little cottage down by the sea shore. And the snow had come.

All day, ceaselessly, it had driven heavily before the north wind; but now the wind had dropped, the sky had cleared, and the little Orkney island of Hoy lay silent, deeply carpeted in fantastic patterns of white.

The ancient wooden cased clock on the mantelshelf above the open peat fire jangled out the midnight chimes, Christmas Day! and the old man reached for his parcel. He knew its contents. There would be the two pairs of warm socks knitted by the laird's wife herself, the little assortment of groceries, the small preserved pudding – and always, on top, the Christmas card – the only card he ever received.

This year it was a big, bonny one: showing a Bedouin fellow atop a white camel, both rider and beast covered in purple and gold trappings, standing on a sea of bright red sand against a deep purple sky – and occupying most of the sky, a large tinsel-dust star; the whole a blaze of colour.

Maybe things were coloured like that in the east, he did not know, but one thing he did know was wrong – that star! – a four-pointed affair with tinsel glitter beams emanating from its cardinal points to the edges and top of the card.

He knew the stars, a great many by name, and the constellations too. Each year at springtime he was the night shepherd up on the moor. For a whole six weeks he was out there with the stars, they were his companions, his friends; and this four-pointed glittering tinsel thing with its four long shafts – never!

He rose from his stool and placed the card on the mantelshelf beside the clock, for now he would go to his bed, where, on most nights of the year, he would have been three hours ago. He thought the card looked even better now; the star and its four shafts glittered, even in the paraffin lamplight. Yes, it was a bonny card!

With the suddenness of an explosion in the silence of the cottage came the heavy beat of a fist against the door. For a moment the old man did not move: people very rarely came down here to the cottage; and now, at this late hour, and through those deep drifts ....

He turned up the flame of the little lamp and crossed to the door, stood surveying it uncertainly for some moments; then, throwing off the heavy oak crossbar, he pulled the door wide.

Soaking wet and knee-deep in snow stood the young tinker, sweating, breathing heavily, the coarse open sleeveless shirt exposing a deep chest and powerful arms, the shock of raven-black hair matted above the dark burning eyes. The old shepherd recognised him at once, had seen him a day or two back up there at the 'Watery Slap', at a tent rigged under the stunted willows. He had noticed, too, the young gypsy woman with him. They had been there three days, and he'd expected them to be gone by the morning boat – over to the main island to join their kin for the year's end celebrations; but something had delayed them, and heavy snow had come and closed the long road. He would know in a moment what had delayed them, for the gypsy was speaking; quietly, but with a note of urgency:

'Gie's a haun wi' ma wumman, mister – the bairn's comin.'

The old shepherd looked into the other's swarthy face.

'Is it close?'

'Aye mister, close enough.'

The old man turned towards his single iron bedstead. He did not ask why they had missed the early morning boat or why they had travelled with the event so close. Knowing the tinkers, he was certain some unforeseen calamity had befallen them, and as if reading the older man's thoughts the gypsy said,

'It's a month ower early, mister.'

So the couple had been caught by the sudden fall; he knew the tinker would not leave his woman to walk the five miles to the doctor's house – knowing the road would be completely blocked for either of them to return. In blind faith he had waited until now, and the old man was pleased he had come.

Throwing off the rough blankets, he lashed the straw mattress to the wire frame of the bed, and kicked the frame out of the bed ends; then, by common understanding that the woman must be brought to the shelter of the cottage, the two men lifted it and went out into the silver, blue, starlit night.

The shepherd picked his way down the beach through the long drifts to the sea's edge, the gypsy placing his feet precisely in the old man's tracks. At the snow-free, ice-bound margin of the shore, the shepherd stopped. He had noticed the younger man's heavy limp up in the cottage, and he knew he was hurt. Half turning his head, he asked,

'You all right, boy?'

'Aye mister – ah'm fine.'

The old man led on over the frozen sea wrack, the uneven gait of the tinker as his iron-studded boots rang on the ice-covered stones telling that the other was in pain. It was going to be a tough job, and at seventy years he wondered if his own strength would last. At the burn mouth, two hundred yards along the shore, the old man halted for breath. Here, he decided, they would leave the shore and go straight up the steep hundred-yard bank. He had been wondering how the tinker had reached the cottage over that deep deceptive carpet of snow – and now he could see how it had been achieved, and why the gypsy was hurt. From here he could see the tops of the snow-covered willows up at the Watery Slap. He saw the footprints of the man coming over the rise in the snowbank, then ending suddenly in an almost circular hole – the gypsy had missed the little stone bridge by inches! The burn, a series of waterfalls and ledges, ran some eight feet below surface level, its perpendicular sides gouged by centuries of torrent and its top almost concealed by the long heather meeting from its sides. This, covered by deep snow, the gypsy had missed, and slipped through; and had been forced to make the incredible hundred-yard journey down the burn – over the slippery boulders and icy pools to the shore, all in darkness!

The old shepherd stood silent, regarding the other in speechless wonder. With a note of impatience the gypsy said,

'Ready, mister?'

Slowly the men climbed the rise. At the top the shepherd stopped for breath. Vaguely he could make out the roof of the little tent in the shadow of the willows, the small paraffin lamp within showing thinly through the canvas, the snow built high about the perimeter of the trees, the star-encrusted backdrop of the sky – and the silence, broken only by the laboured breathing of the two men.

The gypsy girl lay on a bed of heather fronds beneath a pair of grey blankets. Kneeling, and taking the woman's hands between his own, the gypsy said, very softly,

'We're takin ye awa, lassie – dinna be feart.'

The shepherd saw the woman's hands tighten on the man's; only the eyes showed her resigned acceptance of the situation as the men lifted her gently onto the wire bed, the young man covering her with the blankets and a square of old canvas.

With the old man leading, the little party began the return journey, stepping exactly in the tracks they had already made – more slowly now; the shepherd could feel the pronounced limp of the gypsy, and his own exhaustion, becoming more acute. At the foot of the slope he stopped. Turning, he said through gulps of breath,

'Sorry, boy – I'm out of breath.'

At once the other returned,

'Ye're daen fine, mister – jist fine.'

The shepherd again looked at the hole in the snow at the burnmouth, where the gypsy had broken through. He understood the fierce determination that had driven him down that treacherous gully. It reminded him of the dog otter, many years before, in this very burnmouth, when the big sheepdog had tried to flush him from his holt, and he had come out and stood his ground, teeth bared, claws unsheathed, ready to grapple in the deathlock in defence of his mate and young whelps, and the big sheepdog had backed down.

He was a bachelor himself, but for almost sixty years he had lived with nature up there on the moor with the two great elemental forces, the Male and the Female.

He looked down at the woman, lying quietly, the dark eyes closed – the female, trusting her mate implicitly.

The soft urgent voice of the gypsy cut across his thoughts.

'Ready, mister?'

The journey was easier now, the frozen sea wrack popping and crackling beneath the heavy iron-shod boots.

Almost an hour had passed since the men had begun their journey, and now they returned, setting their burden on the stone-flagged cottage floor.

The old shepherd kicked the peat fire into life and swung over the great iron boiling pot on its heavy chain; then both men sat, silent.

Just before the first light of dawn, it was over. To the old shepherd, deliverer of countless new-born creatures, it had been the same.

With infinite care he attended to and washed the male child and placed it gently into the opened arms of the girl.

Taking the tin of milk from his Christmas parcel, he mixed and warmed some, poured it into a cup, and placed it within reach of the woman; then, as if to give her a moment of seclusion, the two men, by mutual understanding, moved quietly to the cottage door and went out into the night.

No word had been spoken by either man since they had returned to the cottage, but now, standing outside the door, the gypsy said, quietly,

'Thank ye, mister.'

Above and around them widened the vast blue night. Facing the East, the two men of the outdoors watched in silence as the golden strip of first light came up and the frosty stars faded. The obscurity of night was passing, leaving only the morning star, scintillating, alone. The old man thought of his bonny card, and reflected it was shepherds too that had seen that first Christmas star: they would not have seen a large, four-pointed affair – they would have seen it as he saw it now, a bright shimmering point of light set against the purple, luminous sky.

His train of thought was broken by the sob of the gypsy by his side. Turning his head, he met the young man's eyes; he saw the tear of thankfulness run down the brown unshaven face and fall onto the bared chest. He noticed the emotion in the voice as again the other said,

'Thank ye, mister.'

The old shepherd felt a sudden hot stinging in his own eyes, and a hurting tightness about his throat. Quickly turning his head, he tried to stifle his emotion by steadying his gaze on the morning star – and through the tear of compassion that suddenly filled his old eyes, he saw it swell to a glittering orb, then shoot out four bright shafts of light – just like the star on his Christmas card.

A TOUCH OF MUSIC

I DIDN'T REALLY PLAY ANY INSTRUMENTS.

Well, only the saxophone. I bought one second-hand in Hong Kong in 1926, cost me 200 Mexican dollars. Sounds a lot, eh? Oh yes, and I bought a 2/6d. sax tutor and I learnt the instrument and music together.

I like other musical instruments though; yes, even pipes, especially the Northumbrian ones – very sweet they are. I like the Irish pipes too, but I'm not awfully fond of the Scottish pipes; it's a matter of taste, I suppose. I guess I like the Scottish bagpipes as much as a Scottish bagpipe player would like a bowl of Cockney jellied eels ....

But speaking of pipes, our minister in Hoy, Rev. Ewen Traill, was giving the kids a mini-sermon one Sunday and he was telling them a story about bagpipes. It was true, he said; and it was such a fantastic yarn, that I couldn't stop thinking about it. And here it is – well, my version of it.

In the 19th century there was a ship which sailed for Australia with a general cargo and a dozen passengers – emigrants. Going down the West African coast she struck a reef and began to sink. The captain – he was a Scot, y'see – seeing that nothing could be done to save his ship, gave the order to abandon ship. Well, the passengers and crew manned the two lifeboats and lay off the ship while the captain stayed on board on the quarter-deck,standing to attention facing forward.

The people in the boats watched the water gradually rise till it got to his ankles. I suppose they said: 'What a brave chiel, he's going to go down with the ship.'

Now, you've heard about the captain who played his ukelele as the ship went down – well, this Scottish captain suddenly turned around and went into his cabin, y'see, and he came out with a set of bagpipes. He tucked them under his arm and began to play. Of course, all the people in the boats thought he was a braver chiel than ever and I suppose if it wasn't for the sake of rocking the boats, they would have got up and given him a standing ovation, as they say.

Well, he kept on playing these pipes until the water reached his armpits; and when his feet and the deck parted company, he just floated off on his inflated bagpipes, using them as a lifebuoy. And lifting the chanter above water, I suppose, he just stood there treading water until he had finished this here particular tune he was playing. I suppose it was *Will Ye No' Come Back Again* or something. Anyway, these people in the lifeboats thought that when he'd finished playing, he'd let go of the bagpipes and sink, singing *Auld Lang Syne* or something like that. But no – he was a right canny Scot; he just shoved his chanter under the water and paddled himself ashore.

(That was the first part of the story – and I didn't believe a word of it; but the story continued like this ....)

When everyone got ashore,they were all wet and miserable – they couldn't light a fire because all their matches were wet and their tinder boxes were full of seaweed and all that sort of thing. Ah, but the captain soon put that right; he formed them up into eights, emptied the water out of his pipes and struck up an Eightsome Reel. Well, after a couple of reels everybody was cheerful and happy and their clothes had dried off a bit.

(That was the second bit of the story and I didn't believe that either.)

Ah, but those pipes came in handy again, y'see, because that night they all sat huddled together on the open beach (still without a fire) and all the beasts of the jungle – y'know there was a lot of beasts of the jungle then – they all came down to the edge of the trees; y'know, lions and tigers and pumas and leopards and wildebeest and dirty-beest, they all stood around, waiting there, smacking their chops in anticipation of a nice fresh Scottish supper, y'see.

And they were just closing in when the skipper grabbed his pipes and started playing and all these animals suddenly disappeared back into the jungle!

Well, I believed that! Yeh, that's one part of the story I *did* believe!

Y'know, to hear a set of bagpipes suddenly strike up in the dead of night – blimey – that's enough to scare the living daylights out of any creature!

THE MASTERPIECE

EBBTIDE the beachcomber, with the merest tightening of the rein, stopped the thirty-year-old Clydesdale Titus and waited for the island laird to speak from the opened window of the shooting-brake that screeched to a halt beside him on the narrow island road. Sticking his head out of the window and looking up into the beachcomber's face, the laird barked,

'We're looking for a ship's wheel, Ebbtide – got one?'

The old man nodded. The laird went on:

'Good – visiting friend of mine here – retired master mariner – is lookin' for one for drawing-room decor, y'know.'

Looking up into the leathery face, he added

'No need for you to come back, Ebbtide – we'll find it – y'don't mind us lookin' around your cottage?'

The beachcomber smiled and gently woke the now sleeping horse with a tap of the rein.

The laird, the retired ship's master, and a younger male visitor from the south entered, Indian file, into the beachcomber's cottage, packed to its blackened wooden rafters with miscellaneous flotsam and jetsam, ships' furniture, buoys, rope, junk, all seasoned with ages of peat smoke and overlaid with a heavy coat of grime.

To the younger man this was an Aladdin's cave, an antique dealer's Shangri La. The laird had said that a former visitor to the cottage had even found a carved quarterdeck panel that had come from a Spanish Armada galleon. Somewhere among that conglomeration of bits and pieces was the ship's wheel. Luckily, its brass-capped midship spoke was quickly spotted by the laird near the top of the pile, and while pulling the thing out the younger man discovered the strained artist's flax canvas.

Taking it out into the daylight, he gently tapped off the dust, and there, under a yellow-brown layer of peat smoke, he beheld a masterpiece that had no doubt washed ashore from some wreck. He propped it against the cottage wall. Obliquely, and from between narrowed lids, he scrutinised the painting – looking for a signature; the others watched in silence. Softly, he said: 'It's beautiful – abstract expressionism – a powerful painting!' He up-ended the painting, and again whispered: 'It's beautiful.'

Turning to the laird, he asked:

'D'you know where it might have come from?'

The laird coughed, glared at the canvas, then:

'I think it came ashore from the *Kathe Kirchneider,* an East German that went up on the skerries – lot o' junk washed up out of her.'

The young man spread his hands in a deprecatory gesture.

'Well,' the laird went on quickly, 'Dunno what you see in a thing like that.' Affecting to be overcome by the other's ignorance in art matters, the young man tapped the canvas, then:

'This is not junk – it is painting reduced to the physical act – a revolt against the traditional idea – an experiment by the artist in abstract – !'

'All right, all right,' the laird cut in. 'If you think it's that good, you'd better take it. Ebbtide would probably boil his kettle with it, anyway.'

The master mariner looked at his watch.

'We'll have to be going – our smallboat will be waiting. How much should I leave for the wheel?'

'A hundred would please Ebbtide,' the laird clipped.

'And I'll leave a hundred for the painting,' the young man volunteered.

It was the next day that the laird met up with Ebbtide. Calling the old man across, he handed him two one-hundred-pound cheques. The beachcomber, clearly overcome by such a large sum, looked puzzled, then:

'They gonna 'ave half that wheel each?' he jested. The laird laughed.

'A hundred for the wheel, an' a hundred for the painting.'

'Painting? '

'Yes, the painting that washed up from the *Kathe Kirchneider.*'

'If you mean that canvas – it was a blank canvas – nothing on it.'

'But there *was* a painting on it, Ebbtide – evidently a very good one. '

Ebbtide scratched his ear thoughtfully.

'No, my sight's not *that* bad. If there had been a painting on it, I wouldn't have used that canvas to rub out me brushes after I'd tarred and painted me dinghy.'